MORPHOLOGY AND EVOLUTION
OF FOSSIL PLANTS

These Studies are designed to inform the mature student — the undergraduate upperclassman and the beginning graduate student — of the outstanding advances made in various areas of modern biology. The books will not be treatises but rather will briefly summarize significant information in a given field and interpret it in terms of our current knowledge of the rapidly expanding research findings within the life sciences. Also it is hoped that the Studies will be of interest to teachers and research workers.

BIOLOGY STUDIES ←

Bell, *Ultrasound in Biology*

Carlquist, *Comparative Plant Anatomy*

Carpenter, *Fossil Insects and Evolution*

Crafts, *Translocation in Plants*

Deevey, *Historical Ecology*

Delevoryas, *Morphology and Evolution of Fossil Plants*

Hillman, *The Physiology of Flowering*

Slobodkin, *Growth and Regulation of Animal Populations*

Sutton, *Genes, Enzymes, and Inherited Diseases*

Theodore Delevoryas
Yale University

MORPHOLOGY AND EVOLUTION
OF FOSSIL PLANTS

Holt, Rinehart
and Winston
*New York, Chicago,
San Francisco,
Toronto, London*

▶
▶
▶
▶ **TO OSWALD TIPPO,**
▶
▶   *teacher,*

        counselor,

        friend

4   5   6   7   8   9

COPYRIGHT © 1962 BY HOLT, RINEHART AND WINSTON, INC.
ALL RIGHTS RESERVED
LIBRARY OF CONGRESS CATALOG CARD NUMBER: 62-20103

2116309

PRINTED IN THE UNITED STATES OF AMERICA

preface ▶▶▶▶▶

Paleobotany, like other scientific disciplines, is becoming more diversified, with different workers in the field professing a variety of aims and goals. Thus, some paleobotanists study fossil plants to learn from them ecological and climatological conditions and changes in past ages. Others are concerned with floral changes and migrations as recorded by the rocks. Some approach the subject from a geological standpoint, using fossil plants only as aids in determining geological sequences and ages of strata containing them. The study of microfossils such as spores and pollen grains has increased in popularity, and many paleobotanists are concerned with the various problems they present.

It is the morphological and evolutionary viewpoint that is emphasized in this volume. From fossil plants, paleobotanists realize the former existence of plant forms, the evolution of which can be traced through hundreds of millions of years. Origins also are of interest to the morphological paleobotanist.

The approach to this aspect of paleobotany is primarily through comparative morphology. To this study is added the dimension of time, with the accompanying myriads of plants not represented in comparative studies of extant plants only.

Perhaps it will be noticed that equal emphasis is not given to all groups of fossil plants. Admittedly, this may be due in part, consciously or unconsciously, to the special interests of the author. More important, however, is the fact that thorough morphological investigations have not yet been done on all fossil taxa, even though other plant groups have been the subjects of intensive studies, including attempts to determine ontogenetic development of some of the extinct plants. These ontogenetic studies shed considerable light on possible sequences of development in the fossils that are quite different from those in many modern forms.

Although they are the most important group of plants today, the angiosperms have not been afforded much space in this book. This limited treatment does not reflect a lack of interest in the group on the author's part; but rather because almost all fossil angiosperms are identical with or extremely similar to modern representatives of the class, a morphological treatise on that group would resemble a text on higher plant anatomy or on the morphology of angiosperms. Since so little of morphological trends among the fossil angiosperms is known at this time, it is not possible to make a comparative study of extinct forms. Similarly, more recent members of other taxa have been less emphasized because in general structure they closely approximate their modern counterparts.

A book of this size can in no way be considered complete. It has been necessary to omit reference to a considerable amount of modern work on fossil plants in an attempt to survey, in this limited space, the effect of recent developments in the field on older classical work in paleobotany. Whenever possible, the newer literature is cited, even though older papers may be better known. Important earlier works, however, are also included.

The author is grateful to the many researchers and publishers who have kindly permitted him to use previously published material. A number of illustrations have been redrawn by the author; others are used in their original form. Most of the photographs have not been used before, but acknowledgment is made for those that have.

The stimulus of conversations and discussions that the author has had with colleagues, students, and former students has contributed to the formulation of many of the concepts presented here. Special thanks are due Dr. Wilson N. Stewart, colleague and former teacher, and Dr. Donald A. Eggert, a former student, who have influenced my thinking concerning many of the ideas reflected here. Appreciation is extended to Dr. Tom L. Phillips, who kindly read the entire manuscript and offered valuable suggestions. The author, however, is responsible for all of the interpretations, correct or incorrect, that appear in this volume.

T. D.

New Haven, Connecticut
June, 1962

contents

chapter one ▸ Introduction

The most convincing evidence of plant evolution is the record of fossil plants. Documented deep in the earth's crust are the progressive changes and modifications undergone by various groups of the plant kingdom through millions of years. Every year, students of fossil plants unearth new specimens that help piece together what paleobotanists hope some day will be a continuous story of the development of the plant kingdom from an age more than one billion years ago to the present time. During that long period of time profound changes have occurred in the plant world. Groups have arisen, flourished, and become extinct; without the fossil record present-day botanists would be unaware that such groups of plants ever existed. Also among the fossils can be read early beginnings of some of the present-day groups, many of which are mere remnants of once significant assemblages. One of the milestones in the evolution of the plant kingdom is the invasion of the land by aquatic types. Early land plant fossils dramatically show how this might have come about. Changes in the earth's climate and the subsequent effect on floras can also be read from the records.

By no means is the fossil record complete, however. There are many gaps, and even though the gaps become fewer or less pronounced, a large number still remain. What are the reasons for these breaks? A brief consideration of how and where plant fossils are formed may help to explain why the record is incomplete.

1

KINDS OF PRESERVATION

Plants are preserved in the earth's crust in various ways, and each of the different types of preservation requires its own technique for study. Perhaps the most common kind of preservation is the *compression*. A compression is formed when a plant or plant part is somehow buried and covered with sediments of various kinds. As the name suggests, there occurs a flattening of the plant parts due to the weight of the sediments. The end result is a thin, carbonaceous film with the outlines and surface features of the plant parts. Generally, little or no internal cellular detail is preserved. Sediments of various kinds may be involved as matrices for compressions. Shale, sandstone, volcanic ash, and diatomaceous earth are some of the types of matrices. Generally speaking, the finer grained the matrix, the more exquisite the preservation — assuming the plant parts were covered quickly. Minute surface details can be seen on compressions in fine-grained shale or in diatomite, for example.

Many compressions lend themselves only to a study of the external appearances of plant parts. In many instances, however, in addition to the carbonaceous film there is preserved the original cuticle, the waxy layer that covers leaves and other organs of plants. This cuticle may be isolated, cleared, and mounted to reveal minute surface details such as stomatal structure and distribution, epidermal cell characteristics, and structure and distribution of hairs or trichomes. Many significant contributions to paleobotany have been made by a careful study of fossil cuticles (Fig. 1-1).

Sometimes it is possible to transfer the cuticle on to a film of cellulose acetate, using a liquid material such as fingernail polish or collodion. This transfer can then be cleared and mounted on a slide for microscopic examination.

Coal is usually considered to be a complex kind of compression. Coal is formed by an extensive accumulation of plant material, in a basin of water, that is gradually compressed. It is generally thought that a tremendous amount of compaction occurs, and this can be testified by the structural details of coal. Coal can be studied by viewing it in reflected light, by grinding thin sec-

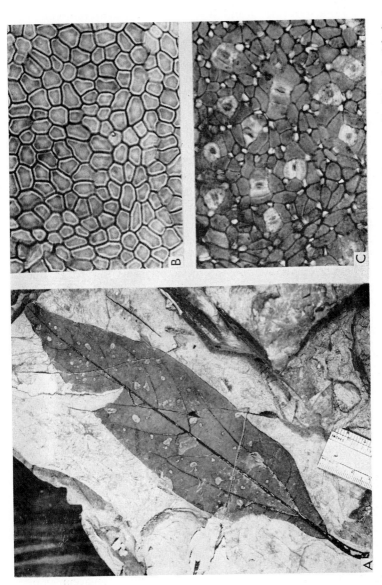

Fig. 1-1. Examples of compression fossils. A, leaf of *Ocotea obtusifolia* from the Eocene of Tennessee; B, slide of cuticle from upper epidermis of a leaf of *O. obtusifolia*; C, cuticle from lower epidermis of a similar leaf. (Photographs courtesy of David L. Dilcher.)

3

tions, or by macerating it and isolating the resistant components. Among plant parts found in coal are spores, wood fragments, bark fragments, cuticles, and resins.

Paper coal is an unusual type of preservation in which the coal consists almost entirely of layer after layer of cuticle. These cuticles may be separated and mounted on slides, often with impressive results.

An *impression* may best be thought of as the negative of a compression. Sediments that cover and compress plant parts may harden, and when split open at the region of the fossil they show the negative imprint of the plant part. No organic material and, hence, no cellular detail are visible, but the outlines of the plant parts are readily discernible. Undoubtedly readers are familiar with the imprints of leaves that have fallen on freshly poured concrete sidewalks. These imprints, formed as the concrete hardens, are actually impressions, or the negatives of the leaves. As one would expect, better details are present on impressions formed in fine-grained matrices.

When there has been only a little compression, or none at all, the sedimentary material surrounding a plant part may harden to form a three-dimensional *mold*. Furthermore, after the mold is hardened to some extent, the plant part may decay and dis-integrate, and the space formerly occupied by the plant part is filled in with other sediments. These harden to form a *cast,* which has the same external configurations as the original plant fragment. Molds and casts show no cellular detail and generally lack any of the original organic material in the plant. They are valuable to paleobotanists, however, in reconstructing the external appearance of many kinds of plants.

An interesting type of preservation, and one that allows a study of the internal structure of organisms, is the *petrifaction*. Petrifaction was at one time thought to involve a molecule-by-molecule replacement of the plant part by minerals in solution that eventually hardened. In other words, the cells of the plant were thought to have been replaced a molecule at a time by rock. In many instances there has been almost complete replacement of organic material by the matrix. The famous fossil logs in the Petrified Forest National Monument in Arizona generally show poor internal structure because the cells have been replaced by silica. This has not been a molecule-by-molecule replacement, however. In contrast, in well-preserved petrified material the infiltrating substance crystallizes and hardens in the cell lumens and intercellular spaces, effectively embedding the plant fragments in a hard matrix. This matrix may be calcium, magnesium, or iron carbonate; silica; calcium or magnesium phosphate; iron pyrite; or any combination of these. It has been possible to dissolve away the matrix of some petrifactions, embed them in celloidin, and section them on an ordinary sliding microtome, demonstrating clearly that most of the cell-wall material is still intact.

Because cellular details are preserved, petrifactions can be studied by making sections of them. The standard technique is a tedious one, but excellent results are obtainable. A small piece of the petrified material is cut out with a saw that has either a diamond-edged blade or a carborundum blade. The surface from which the section is to be made is polished and mounted on a glass slide with a transparent adhesive. The specimen is then cut again, leaving as thin a section as possible adhering to the slide. Grinding and polishing will eventually make the rock section thin enough to allow light to pass through, making it possible to view the fossil under a microscope with transmitted light.

With certain kinds of matrices, however, a much simpler technique may be used. Petrifactions with a calcium or magnesium carbonate matrix are polished and the surfaces then dipped into dilute hydrochloric acid. Acid etches away the carbonate, leaving the cell walls projecting in relief. After the surface has been washed and allowed to dry, a thick nitrocellulose solution is poured on the leveled surface. The acetate fills the slightly hollowed-out lumens and intercellular spaces and is allowed to dry. A more recent technique calls for a prepared acetate sheet to be gently laid on the surface of the fossil, which has been wet with acetone. In either case, after the acetate has hardened, it can be pulled off, taking with it a very thin section of the petrifaction. These "peels" can then be cleared, mounted on slides, and examined microscopically. When the matrix is silica, hydrofluoric acid must be used instead. Many kinds of matrices do not lend themselves to the peel technique, and it is necessary to prepare ground thin sections. When the crumbly nature of the fossil or the opacity of the material prevents making thin sections, reflected light studies on polished surfaces are carried out.

Another way in which plant parts are found as fossils is in a relatively *unaltered* state. A plant fragment may have fallen into a body of water and then been covered with fine-grained sediment that excludes air and decaying organisms. Often there is little or no compression of the material, nor do the parts become petrified. After millions of years a piece of wood thus preserved may be embedded in celloidin and sectioned as any modern tissue would be. Certain of the standard staining procedures may also be followed.

There are still other ways in which fossil plants may be preserved. The extensive deposits of diatomaceous earth in some parts of the world represent areas that had been once inundated by seas that contained countless billions of tiny, one-celled algae with exquisitely sculptured siliceous walls. After the organisms died, the glass shells slowly sank to the bottom, there to contribute more and more minute particles to the very slowly accumulating mass of shells. These shells are preserved intact, and a microscopic mount of diatomaceous earth shows the fine detail on the siliceous frustules.

Evidences of other kinds of algae show up in still another kind of fossilization. Many algae secrete around themselves a heavy coat of calcium carbonate. Indeed, it is now generally recognized that the so-called "coral reefs" in warm oceanic waters are built up more by accumulation of calcium carbonate produced by algae than by the corals themselves. Calcium carbonate accumulated by algae may persist for millions of years, and a study of these calcified masses reveals the structure of the algae contained within them.

The above discussion does not present every conceivable way by which plants become fossilized, but most of the more important processes involved have been listed.

CONDITIONS FOR FOSSILIZATION

It at once becomes obvious why the fossil record is not a complete one. Several important conditions must be met if a plant is to become fossilized. Generally, the plant part must be in a region where deposition is taking place; if it is not, it must somehow be transported to a region where sediments are accumulating. Thus many plants growing in upland, exposed regions would naturally fail to meet this condition. As a result the fossil

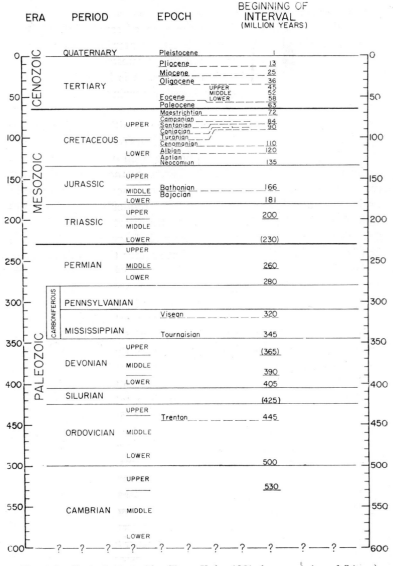

Fig. 1-2. Geologic timetable. (From Kulp, 1961; by permission of *Science*.)

record probably gives a somewhat distorted picture of what floras were actually like at certain times, since all plants growing at the time are not represented as fossils.

Another requirement is the presence of some kind of body of water. It is generally believed that the water in some instances must have been charged with antiseptic substances that slowed down the decay of the organic materials. It is in such a body of water, whether it be fresh, brackish, or marine, that deposition took place.

Even if the plant part did become fossilized, other factors limit its value to the paleobotanist. Coarse sediments produce compressions that are generally not so well preserved as compressions in fine-grained rock. Furthermore, the cuticle may not have been preserved. In petrified specimens, enough decomposition may have occurred before fossilization to render the specimen unusable for critical study. Plant parts transported some distances before they are fossilized are often extremely fragmentary. Also to be taken into consideration is the fact that regions that had once been centers of deposition may at later times have been elevated, and thus erosion eliminated what fossils may have been formed previously in that region. All these, and other factors, then, limit the amount of material a paleobotanist has to work with.

Nevertheless, the story told by the fossils, incomplete though it may be, is an impressive one and one that contributes immeasurably to an understanding of plant evolution.

Because there will be frequent reference to the geologic ages of the plant fossils discussed, a geologic time table, indicating the sequences of geologic periods and the approximate number of years to the beginning of each period or series, has been included in this book (Fig. 1-2).

REFERENCES

Abbott, Maxine L., 1950. "A paleobotanical transfer method," *J. Paleont.*, **24**: 619–621.

Abbott, R. E., and Maxine L. Abbott, 1952. "A simple paleobotanical transfer technique," *Ohio J. Sci.*, **52**: 258–260.

Arnold, C. A., 1941. "The petrifaction of wood," *The Mineralogist*, **9**.

Beck, C. B., 1955. "A technique for obtaining polished surfaces of sections of pyritized plant fossils," *Bull. Torrey Botan. Club,* **82:** 286–291.

Darrah, W. C., 1936. "The peel method in paleobotany," *Harvard Univ. Botan., Mus. Leafl.,* **4:** 69–83.

——, 1952. "The materials and methods of paleobotany," *Palaeobotanist,* **1:** 145–153.

Harris, T. M., 1956. "The fossil plant cuticle," *Endeavor,* **15:** 210–214.

Joy, K. W., A. J. Willis, and W. S. Lacey, 1956. "A rapid cellulose peel technique in palaeobotany," *Ann. Botan.,* n.s., **20:** 635–637.

Kräusel, R., 1950. *Die paläobotanischen Untersuchungsmethoden,* Jena: Gustav Fischer.

Kulp, J. L., 1961. "Geologic time scale," *Science,* **133:** 1105–1114.

Lacey, W. S., 1953. "Methods in palaeobotany," *North Western Nat.,* **24:** 234–249.

Walton, J., 1923. "On a new method of investigating fossil plant impressions or incrustations," *Ann. Botan.,* **37:** 379–391.

——, 1928. "Recent developments in palaeobotanical technique," *Compte Rendu, Congr. Carb.* Heerlen, l'Avanc. Étude Strat. (1927): 749–754.

——, 1928. "A method of preparing sections of fossil plants contained in coal balls or in other types of petrifaction," *Nature,* **122:** 571.

——, 1936. "On factors which influence external form of fossil plants," *Trans. Roy. Soc. (London),* **226B:** 219–225.

Wesley, A., 1954. "A short synopsis of some microscopical methods in palaeobotany," *Proc. Leeds Phil. Soc.,* **6:** 168–179.

——, and B. Kuyper, 1951. "Electron-microscopic observations on the xylem elements of a fossil plant," *Nature,* **168:** 137–140.

▸
▸
▸
▸
▸
Nonvascular Plants

Algae, fungi, and bryophytes usually occupy a considerable portion of a course on the survey of the plant kingdom. These same groups, however, play a relatively minor role in the discussion of plant evolution as recorded in the rocks because, with the exception of diatoms, fossils of these groups are not abundant. This fact should not be surprising if one considers the fragile nature of these organisms. Most algae and fungi are more than 90 percent water and are so fragile that preservation usually fails. Similarly, liverworts and mosses are delicate and are only occasionally preserved as fossils. Some of the kinds of nonvascular plants found in the fossil record will be considered here because, fragmentary as their record may be, there is some indication of the antiquity of certain of these groups.

In earlier geology texts, the division of the Precambrian and the Cambrian was based on the first appearance of organisms in the rocks. Precambrian deposits were supposed to have been devoid of remains of plants and animals that were usually thought to have made their debut in the Cambrian. At the present time, however, there is indisputable evidence that life existed long before the Paleozoic era. Precambrian coal, supposedly of plant origin, is known in several places in the world. Recent paleobotanical work has revealed structurally preserved plant fragments in Precambrian chert found in Ontario. Among these fossils are small, radiating filaments that resemble a colony of blue-green algae. A sheathlike structure surrounds each algal colony. Other free filaments show some resemblance to other genera of blue-green algae. In addition to the algalike filaments are other, nonseptate filaments resembling fungal hyphae. The exact nature and relationships of these extremely old organisms are still in question, but they are certainly organisms.

Other evidences of Precambrian plant life are indirect but nevertheless impressive. In the vicinity of Glacier National Park are concentrically layered, spherical masses of calcium carbonate deposits. No remains of organisms can be seen, but such calcium carbonate layering is known to occur among certain present-day blue-green algae. The algal colony produces calcium carbonate around itself; the mineral mass continues to expand and the algal colony expands with it. If blue-green algae were indeed responsible for the production of the peculiarly layered limestones, they must have been important constituents of the life in ancient seas. Similarly layered limestones are found in the Cambrian period and are even given generic names (for example, *Cryptozoon*).

Bacteria probably were flourishing in Precambrian times as well. Elongated cell-like structures, resembling the modern bacterial genus *Chlamydothrix*, have been found. Furthermore, the tremendous iron ore deposits of the Precambrian period might have been formed by organisms similar to present-day, iron-depositing bacteria that oxidize ferrous compounds to ferric hydroxide.

Some of the kinds of nonvascular plants found as fossils are listed systematically below.

ALGAE

Cyanophyta

On the basis of the Precambrian chert plants described above, the blue-green algae (Cyanophyta) are the oldest known algae. Records of blue-green, algalike plants are known in later geologic periods as well. The Middle Cambrian genus *Marpolia*, which is very similar to the modern *Schizothrix*, formed a mass of long, radiating, hairlike colonies. *Gloeocapsomorpha* is found in Ordovician deposits, and, as the name implies, bears considerable resemblance to the familiar *Gloeocapsa*. The famous Middle Devonian Rhynie chert of Scotland has yielded remains of an *Oscillatoria*-like alga called *Archaeothrix oscillatoriformis*. Other fossil cyanophyte genera have been described, but in general the structure of the fossil forms is similar to that of modern ones. The fossil record contributes little to our understanding of evolutionary trends in the blue-green algae, although it does demonstrate that the group is an exceedingly ancient one.

Chlorophyta

The green algae, the group from which the higher green plants originated, do not have as long a geologic record as do the blue-greens. Flagellated chlamydomonadlike members, so important as the starting point of several evolutionary lines in the Chlorophyta, are almost completely lacking. This is not surprising, however, considering the delicate nature of those organisms. There is one report of a *Chlamydomonas*-like alga, *Gloeocystis,* from the Upper Jurassic. Its affinities with the chlamydomonads has not been proved, however. *Phacotus,* another flagellated form, is known from the Tertiary.

Desmid zygospores have been found as far back as the Devonian period; Jurassic and Cretaceous ones are also known.

The Paleozoic genera *Pila* and *Reinschia* are of interest because of their association with a kind of coal known as "boghead coal." Earlier workers believed that boghead coal was composed primarily of spores, but it is now almost certain that algal colonies, resembling those of the modern *Botryococcus,* were responsible for this type of coal.

Members of the Codiaceae are known as far back as the Ordovician period.

Among the most abundant green algae preserved as fossils are members of the Dasycladaceae. Because these forms are lime secreting, considerable deposits of calcium carbonate have been produced by the Dasycladaceae. In fact, it is the encrustation of lime that is most frequently found preserved, and sections of the calcium carbonate encrustations reveal the structure of the alga involved (Fig. 2-1B). These plants have coenocytic axes with radiating tubular branches. The fossil record indicates that the group may have been more extensive in the past than is suggested by the ten or so genera of modern forms. The group extends back to the Ordovician, so its history also is a long one.

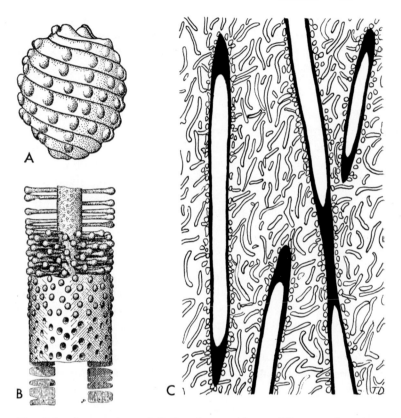

Fig. 2-1. A, oogonium of *Stephanochara compta*, an Oligocene charophyte. (Redrawn from Grambast, 1959b.) B, *Rhabdoporella pachyderma*, an Upper Silurian member of the Siphonocladiales. The upper portion of the diagram shows the alga with the encrusting lime removed. (From Pia, 1927.) C, diagrammatic longitudinal section of *Prototaxites Southworthii*.

Chrysophyta

Members of the Chrysophyta that most frequently appear as fossils are the diatoms. There are occasional reports of diatoms from Paleozoic rocks, but in each case there has not been absolute verification. Unmistakable diatom remains have been found as far back as the Jurassic period, and throughout the Mesozoic and Cenozoic eras they appear in varying abundance. One would be tempted to conclude from the fossil record that the diatoms are not an especially old group, but this is not necessarily the case. Siliceous frustules of diatoms are known to dissolve in alkaline water, and the absence of fossil diatom shells before the Mesozoic era might possibly be due to a failure of preservation.

Charophyta

The charophytes are another algal group with uncertain beginnings in the fossil record. *Palaeonitella* (Middle Devonian) is one of the oldest plant fragments that shows affinities with the Charophyta. Charophyte oogonia (nucules) and zygotes with the characteristic spiral cells are frequently found in Mesozoic and Cenozoic rocks (Fig. 2-1A). These resistant fossil oogonia or zygotes are of interest to micropaleontologists, who use them in stratigraphic studies.

Pyrrophyta

For some years micropaleontologists have been studying certain small bodies, often with spiny or otherwise pronounced, appendages. These structures, called hystrichospheres, seemed to defy classification. It now appears fairly certain, however, that at least some of these hystrichospheres represent cysts of dinoflagellates, members of the Pyrrophyta (Fig. 2-2C). They are found in rocks as old as early Paleozoic, but are more abundant in Mesozoic and Cenozoic deposits.

Phaeophyta

Brown algae are rather rare as fossils, although there are reports of brown algalike organisms having been found in rocks as old as the Devonian. The best known genus of plants that may have affinities with the Phaeophyta is *Prototaxites* (Fig. 2-1C). The Devonian *Prototaxites* has a stout trunklike axis that may be as much as 3 feet in diameter. Making up the huge axis is a system of tightly interlacing tubes of two kinds: larger tubes may be up to 50μ in diameter and are fewer in number than the slender, intertwining tubes, which are generally less than 10μ in diameter. *Nematothallus* is the name applied to flat, leaflike structures that have the same internal structure as *Prototaxites*. Furthermore, there appears to be a cuticle present, as well as spores borne in tetrads within some of the tubes. The general structure of *Prototaxites*

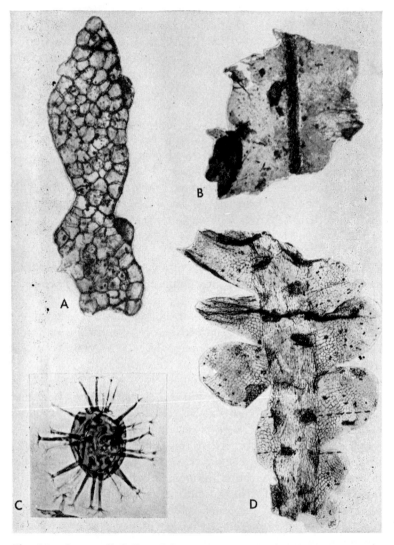

Fig. 2-2. A, a small thallus of *Litostroma oklahomense*. (From Mamay, 1959.) C, *Hystrichosphaeridium recurvatum*, an Upper Cretaceous hystrichosphere with probable dinoflagellate affinities. (From Evitt, 1961.) B, a fragment of the Devonian thallose liverwort, *Hepaticites devonicus*. (From Hueber, 1961.) D, *Hepaticites Kidstoni*, a Carboniferous leafy liverwort. (From Walton, 1925.)

and *Nematothallus,* which some authors consider to be ultimate portions of the former, certainly approaches a brown algal construction, and for this reason these genera are assigned to the Phaeophyta. On the other hand, cuticle and cutinized spores are not associated with a marine habitat, so assignment of *Prototaxites* and *Nematothallus* to the Phaeophyta is tentative.

Rhodophyta

Because many of the red algae are lime secreting, evidence of their former existence is plentiful in the fossil record. Red algal remains are known as far back as the Ordovician. *Solenopora,* a genus that first appears in Ordovician rocks, is an irregularly lobed calcium carbonate mass that shows evidences of filaments when sectioned. Another Ordovician form is *Delesserites,* a leafy form similar to the modern *Delesseria.* Coralline red algae are common in the Mesozoic and Tertiary.

There have also been reports of algae that grew epiphytically on Tertiary leaves; many of these forms are identical with epiphytes on leaves of modern trees.

An algalike fossil, *Litostroma,* that cannot be assigned with any certainty to a definite algal division was described from Middle Pennsylvanian deposits. *Litostroma* (Fig. 2-2A) consists of flat, irregular plates of cells only one cell thick. Occasionally the thallus has perforations.

From the foregoing brief survey of fossil algae, it at once becomes obvious that little can be concluded about the evolution of the various groups. It seems certain that all of the groups are rather old. Many of the fossil forms differ very little structurally from the modern representatives. Scores of algalike fossils have been found, however, that cannot be assigned to any of the presently recognized groups, and perhaps a thorough study of some of these forms may shed some light on algal evolution in past ages, as well as suggest the former existence of algal divisions not found in the waters of today.

FUNGI

Fungal remains are found even less frequently as fossils than are algae. It is usually in association with tissues of higher plants that fungal mycelia are recognized. The report of fungal hyphae from the Precambrian chert, which also yielded blue-green algalike structures, suggests that this group of thallophytes, like the algae, is an old one.

Mycelia and spores occur in relative abundance in tissue of the primitive land plants from the Middle Devonian Rhynie chert. Fungi that appear to be assignable to recent families are recognizable as far back as the Carboniferous period. *Oochytrium*, a supposed member of the Chytridiales, has been found on *Lepidodendron* twigs. *Urophlyctites*, a similar form, has also been seen in tissues of Carboniferous vascular plants. Mucoraceous fungal remains appear to extend back to the Carboniferous period as well. The various fungal groups become increasingly more abundant in later geologic periods, and in the Tertiary scores of forms resembling modern types are known.

Mycorrhizae have been reported by various authors in plants as old as the Devonian.

As with the algae, fungal evolution is not adequately expressed in the fossil record, partly because of the fragmentary nature of the fungal remains, but largely because fungal identifications and relationships are more effectively realized if the entire life history can be observed.

BRYOPHYTA

Most fossil bryophyte identifications can be only tentative because the delicate nature of these organisms is not conducive to completely satisfactory preservation. Furthermore, only fragments of the plants are preserved, and sporophytes are exceedingly rare.

Hepatics appear to have been distinct as far back as the Devonian; a thallose liverwort called *Hepaticites devonicus* has been reported from the Devonian of New York State (Fig. 2-2B). Both thallose and "leafy" forms in the same genus are found in the Carboniferous (Fig. 2-2D). Permian moss fragments have been reported from the Soviet Union. *Naiadita* is an Upper Triassic leafy liverwort with archegonia along the axis, gemma cups at the tips of some of the branches, and globose sporophytes. *Palaeohepatica, Jungermannites, Metzgeriites,* and *Marchantites* are other liverwort genera described from Mesozoic deposits.

Muscites is a moss genus with two Carboniferous species having rather large gametophytes much like those of the common *Polytrichum.* A small axis with rhizoids is also known from the Carboniferous and is significant because of the presence of oblique cross walls in the rhizoids. Many of the late Mesozoic and Tertiary mosses show considerable resemblance to extant types.

A survey of the nonvascular plants seems to indicate that modern morphological types evolved at a very early time, and that changes through hundreds of millions of years have been negligible. This suggestion should not seem unusual after some reflection, since most of the nonvascular plants probably lived in protected and fairly uniform environments. Submerged algae were not exposed to climatologic and physiographic changes as directly as were plants living on land. Fungi, many inhabiting tissues of higher plants, also were protected to a considerable extent and were not subject to fluctuating environments. On the other hand, the examples given deal only with morphological criteria, which are discernible by visual examination. Investigators are currently at a loss to understand what physiological changes might have taken place. Geochemists are convinced that ocean waters have not been uniform since the beginning of life. Factors that varied are pH, temperature, carbon dioxide content, and combinations and proportions of various kinds of salts. These varying conditions must have affected plant and animal life to a considerable degree, and could indeed be expected to produce profound changes in organisms through such long periods of time. An exciting story of nonvascular plant evolution could surely be written if more fossil material were available, and if the physiological modifications resulting from a host of interacting paleo-environmental factors were fully understood.

Not all of the fossils of nonvascular plants are forms directly traceable to modern types. Many of these organisms are morphologically dissimilar to extant types. These forms suggest that many of the nonvascular plant groups were involved in various evolutionary "experiments," many of which proved unsuccessful for long-term survival. *Prototaxites,* although included among the Phaeophyta by many, may represent just such an experiment. It is certainly unlike any known modern types of plants.

Another example of an unaffiliated form is the Devonian genus

Protosalvinia. Only the most distal portions of plants of *Protosalvinia* are known. These stalked, spherical, unlobed or bilobed, cuticle-covered structures were apparently produced at the tips of the plant. In fertile portions of *P. furcata* a furrow lines the two surfaces of the facing lobes. Within this groove is a row of spherical conceptacles, each with a spore tetrad. The resistant spores show triradiate scars when separated. *Protosalvinia* has been assigned to various groups of plants; suggestions concerning its affinities or approximate position in the plant kingdom include algae, intermediate between algae and fungi, intermediate between algae and vascular plants, and level of evolution comparable to that of the Bryophyta.

Parka is a less well-known form from the Upper Silurian and Lower Devonian periods. It is a small, flat, roughly circular thallus with the surface covered with tiny flattened discs containing spores.

The forms described are merely a few examples of the diversity attained by the ancient nonvascular plants and serve to emphasize our ignorance concerning the complete history of the lower plants.

REFERENCES

ANDREWS, H. N., 1960. "Notes on Belgian specimens of *Sporogonites*," *Palaeobotanist,* **7:** 85–89.

ARNOLD, C. A., 1952. "A specimen of *Prototaxites* from the Kettle Point black shale of Ontario," *Palaeontographica,* **93B:** 45–56.

———, 1954. "Fossil sporocarps of the genus *Protosalvinia* Dawson, with special reference to *P. furcata* (Dawson) comb. nov.," *Svensk Botan. Tidskr.,* **48:** 292–300.

BLACKBURN, KATHLEEN, 1936. "A reinvestigation of the alga *Botryococcus Braunii* Kützing," *Trans. Roy. Soc. Edinburgh,* **58:** 841–854.

EVITT, W. R., 1961. "Observations on the morphology of fossil dinoflagellates," *Micropaleontology,* **7:** 385–420.

FENTON, C. L., 1943. "Pre-Cambrian and early Paleozoic algae," *Amer. Midl. Nat.,* **30:** 83–111.

FRY, W. L., and H. P. BANKS, 1955. "Three new genera of algae from the Upper Devonian of New York," *J. Paleont.,* **29:** 37–44.

GRAMBAST, L., 1957. "Ornementation de la gyrogonite et systématique chez les charophytes fossiles," *Rev. Gén. Botan.,* **64:** 1–24.

———, 1959a. "Tendances évolutives dans le phylum charophytes," *Comp. Rend. Acad. Sci.,* **249:** 557–559.

———, 1959b. "Extension chronologique des genres chez les Charoideae," *Soc. Édit. Technip.,* **1959:** 1–12.

Harris, T. M., 1939. "The British Rhaetic flora," *British Mus. Nat. Hist.* 84 pp.

————, 1942. "On two species of Hepaticae of the Yorkshire Jurassic flora," *Ann. Mag. Nat. Hist.*, ser. 11, **9**: 393–401.

Hueber, F. M., 1961. "*Hepaticites devonicus,* a new fossil liverwort from the Devonian of New York," *Ann. Missouri Botan., Gard.,* **48**: 125–132.

Johnson, J. H., 1952. "Ordovician rock-building algae," *Quart. Colo. School Mines,* 47, **no. 3**: 29–56.

————, 1960. "Paleozoic Solenoporaceae and related red algae," *Quart. Colo. School Mines,* 55, **no. 3**: 1–77.

————, 1961. "Studies of Ordovician algae," *Quart. Colo. School Mines,* **56** (2): 1–101.

————, and K. Konishi, 1956. "Studies of Mississippian algae," *Quart. Colo. School Mines,* **51** (4): 1–132.

————, 1958. "Studies of Devonian algae, Part 1, a review of Devonian algae," *Quart. Colo. School Mines* **53** (2): 1–84.

————, 1959. "Studies of Silurian (Gotlandian) algae," *Quart. Colo. School Mines,* **54** (1): 1–114.

Jones, J. D., and J. R. Valentine, 1961. "Biogeochemistry of organic matter — I. Polypeptides and amino acids in fossils and sediments in relation to geochemistry," *Geochim. et Cosmochim.* Acta, **21**: 1–34.

Mamay, S. H., 1959. "*Litostroma,* a new genus of problematical algae from the Pennsylvanian of Oklahoma," *Amer. J. Botan.,* **46**: 283–292.

Neuberg, Maria F., 1955. "Bryophytes from Permian sediments of the U.S.S.R.," *Doklady Akad. Nauk. S.S.S.R.,* **107**: 321–324.

Pia, J., 1927. "Thallophyta" in Hirmer, M., 1927. *Handbuch der Paläobotanik,* Munich and Berlin: R. Oldenbourg.

Temperley, B. N., 1936. "The boghead controversy and the morphology of the boghead algae," *Trans. Roy. Soc. Edinburgh,* **58**: 855–868.

Tyler, S. A., and E. S. Barghoorn, 1954. "Occurrence of structurally preserved plants in pre-Cambrian rocks of the Canadian shield," *Science,* **119**: 606–608.

Walton, J., 1925. "Carboniferous Bryophyta, I. Hepaticae," *Ann. Botan.,* **39**: 563–572.

————, 1928. "Carboniferous Bryophyta, II. Hepaticae and Musci," *Ann. Botan.,* **42**: 707–716.

chapter three ▸ The Appearance of Land Vascular Plants

One of the most significant events in the evolution of the plant kingdom was the invasion of land masses in the early Paleozoic era by primitive vascular plants. The exact period in which this evolutionary step occurred is still not known, but it is generally agreed that it must have been much earlier than the Devonian, because during that period there was considerable diversity of vascular plant forms, suggesting that the land plants had been in existence for some time. Whether the vascular plants, or Tracheophyta, originated from one group of ancestors or whether they evolved from more than one group of nonvascular plants and at different times is also problematical. The great diversity of tracheophytes in Devonian times makes it tempting to believe that the Tracheophyta were polyphyletic, because even as early as that time the lycopod, sphenopsid, and fern lines were distinct. Workers adhering to the polyphyletic point of view argue that because these lines are distinct as far back as they are known, they must have had independent sources.

Other considerations, however, make it appear less likely that more than one group of ancestors are involved. The pigmentation of all of the higher plants is remarkably uniform with regard to chlorophyll kinds and proportions, as well as to other plastid pigments. Furthermore, the carbohydrate storage product is almost always starch. These pigmentation characteristics, as well as features in carbohydrate metabolism, match those of the green algae and are unlike those of any other aquatic nonvascular plant group.

Another feature that the various groups of vascular plants have in common is the structure of the stele. A stele is an effective means of transporting water and minerals from basal regions of a plant to the distal extremities of the aerial portions, and of transporting food materials from the site of their manufacture to the rest of the plant. Such a structure is necessary in plants that no longer inhabit aquatic environs. If the various groups of land vascular plants had independent origins, however, chances of the stelar characteristics evolving in such strikingly similar patterns independently would be small, if not impossible. In almost all vascular plants, the first-formed xylem elements are generally annular and are followed by spiral and scalariform types. In all the groups the progression of stelar type seems to have been from a protostele to a medullated stele.

Probably the most convincing piece of evidence in favor of monophylesis is the nature of the life cycles of the tracheophytes. Life cycles of the vascular cryptogams are almost identical, with a small gametophyte generation that bears archegonia and antheridia alternating with the larger sporophyte. Furthermore, the structure of the archegonium is practically identical in all the forms. In the higher vascular plants, the gametophyte is considerably altered, but its evolution from a free-living generation is obvious.

Until more evidence is forthcoming, then, it appears that a monophyletic point of view is more conservative and more in keeping with what is known about plants, both living and extinct.

If vascular plants have only one origin in geologic time, and evolved from one group of plants, the problem remains as to which were the earliest, most primitive land plants. Lignier suggested in 1903 that land plants evolved from algae with a dichotomizing thallus structure. As the landward migration progressed, one or more of the lateral members of the branching complex entered the soil where they served as organs for anchorage and absorption. As evolution progressed, other portions of the dichotomizing system became flattened, with a progressive webbing forming between the members to form leaflike structures.

Zimmermann refined this idea and extended it with his famous "telome theory." He believed that a three-dimensional dichotomizing system was the basis for all subsequent plant body forms as a result of modifications of this dichotomizing system. By means of this hypothesis, Zimmermann was able to interpret such seemingly diversified structures as lycopsid sporophylls, sphenopsid sporangiophores, fern leaves, and polystelic stems.

Although the concepts of Lignier and Zimmermann are not universally accepted, one fact revealed in the fossil record makes it impossible to discard them completely. Among the earliest vascular plants, the largest number were constructed along the lines of a three-dimensional dichotomous plant body, postulated by Lignier and Zimmermann as the most primitive. In fact, Zimmermann showed that the farther back in the plant fossil record one goes, the larger is the percentage of plants with dichotomous branching systems and terminal sporangia. Admittedly, not enough is known concerning the most primitive vascular plants, but on the basis of present knowledge, Lignier's and Zimmermann's hypotheses have much to recommend them, at least with respect to certain groups of vascular plants.

Although occasional reports appear concerning the occurrence of vascular plants in the Cambrian and Ordovician periods, the earliest undisputed vascular plants are found in rocks of Silurian age. Some of these plants show a relatively high degree of organization, and for that reason are used as evidence against the theories of Lignier and Zimmermann, who suggested that the earliest vascular plants would be expected to be extremely simple in structure. Present knowledge of the earliest vascular plants is meager, however, and thus it certainly cannot be assumed that the very few plants that are known from the Silurian represent a picture of what the entire flora was like. Furthermore, in the Silurian period not all plants were highly specialized, and some actually possessed the simple structure that would be expected.

REFERENCES

References for this chapter are included with those for Chapter Four.

chapter four ► Division
Tracheophyta
Subdivision Psilopsida

Plants of the subdivision Psilopsida are generally leafless (although there may be scalelike emergences on many) and rootless, with dichotomous branching and sporangia borne on the tips of axes. These are the kinds Lignier would have considered to be the most primitive of vascular plants. The group has been recognized for about 50 years, but as paleobotanical research progresses, more and more members are found that are assignable to the subdivision. The only contemporary genera of psilopsids are *Psilotum* and *Tmesipteris* of the order Psilotales.

In 1859 the Canadian geologist Sir J. W. Dawson described plant fragments from the Devonian deposits of the Gaspé Peninsula. The compression fossils were extremely fragmentary, but from them Dawson reconstructed plants composed of slender dichotomizing aerial axes arising from a rhizome system on which were borne rhizoids. Parts of the aerial stems had spinelike emergences, and the branches tapered to very slender axes, on the tips of some of which were borne paired, pendant sporangia. He was also able to isolate fragments of vascular elements from some of the axes, proving that a stele was present. Because of the supposed resemblance to the *Psilotum* of today, Dawson named the new discovery *Psilophyton princeps*.

24

There was a general reluctance among botanists to accept Dawson's discovery because of the fragmentary nature of the fossil specimens and because his reconstruction revealed such an unusual kind of plant. In fact, many texts published after Dawson's discovery neglected to mention it at all.

Dawson's conclusions were essentially substantiated with the appearance of a series of papers commencing in 1917 by R. Kidston and W. H. Lang in which are described primitive vascular plants from beds of the Old Red Sandstone in Aberdeenshire, Scotland. The exact age of the chert in which the petrified plants occur is yet to be determined, but it is certainly no younger than Middle Devonian. These plants had a general structure not unlike that of *Psilophyton,* and for these primitive plants, including *Psilophyton,* that are "characterised by the sporangia being borne at the ends of certain branches of the stem without any relation to leaves or leaf-like organs" (Kidston and Lang, 1917), the order Psilophytales was instituted. Two families are recognized from the Old Red Sandstone plants: one is the Rhyniaceae, with the genera *Rhynia* (after the town Rhynie) and *Horneophyton*[1]; the other, the Asteroxylaceae, with the single genus *Asteroxylon.*

Rhynia Gwynne-Vaughani (Fig. 4-1A) was a slender plant with aerial, dichotomizing, leafless stems arising from a horizontal rhizome with rhizoids on the lower side. It was thought to have reached a height of about 17 cm; at the tips of some of the slender axes were sporangia 3 or more mm long and 1 to 1.5 mm thick. They were homosporous, with many of the spores still in quartets. On the surface of the stem were small, hemispherical projections to some of which were attached structures thought to have been adventitious branches.

Rhynia major is the larger of the two species in the genus. It was thought to have attained a height about three times that of *R. Gwynne-Vaughani.* Hemispherical projections and adventitious branches are lacking, but in general the habit is like that of the smaller species. Sporangia up to 12 by 4 mm and containing spores of one size terminated some of the dichotomizing axes.

Horneophyton Lignieri is thought to have been smaller than *Rhynia Gwynne-Vaughani* and differed from *Rhynia* in that it had a

---

[1] The name *Hornea* had been used by Kidston and Lang, but because it had been used before, the generic designation is now *Horneophyton.*

Fig. 4-1. A, reconstruction of *Rhynia Gwynne-Vaughani.* (Courtesy Chicago Museum of Natural History.) B, longitudinal section of the sporangium of *Horneophyton Lignieri* showing the tip of the stem axis, the thick sporangium wall, the columella, and the spores. C, compressed synangium of *Yarravia oblonga.* (From Lang and Cookson, 1935.)

lobed, unvascularized, rhizoid-covered rhizome from which originated dichotomously branched, slender, aerial stems not exceeding 2 mm in diameter. Terminating some of the slender branches were small, homosporous sporangia, each with a sterile columella projecting into the sporangial cavity from the base (Fig. 4-1B). It is interesting to note that the columella is continuous with the phloem of the stele below.

Asteroxylon is by far the most complicated, as well as the largest, genus in the Old Red Sandstone flora. The basal portion of *A. Mackiei* consisted of a naked rhizome bearing dichotomizing, root-like branches. Aerial shoots were densely clothed with leaflike scales that lacked vascularization. Branching of the main aerial shoots does not appear to have been dichotomous, although lateral branches fork more or less into equal members. In the rhizome the vascular system is haplostelic, becoming conspicuously actino-stelic in the aerial stems (hence the name *Asteroxylon*). Primary xylem is mesarch and protoxylem is situated near the tips of the arms of the xylem strand. Although traces originated at the tips of the arms and bent upward and outward toward the scales, the bundles did not actually enter the scales but stopped in the outer cortex. Stomata are present in the epidermis of the stem. No sporangia have been seen attached to the plant, but it is thought that the fertile branches of *A. Mackiei* were leafless and slender and terminated in small, pear-shaped sporangia.

Another species, *A. elberfeldense,* has been reported from the Middle Devonian of Germany (Fig. 4-2A). Its aerial stems reached over a meter in height, and may have been more than 1 cm thick. The rhizome was irregularly or dichotomously branched, with some of the lateral members functioning as roots. The aerial stem was dichotomous or sympodial and covered with leaflike scales in the basal portions; the upper part, consisting of very slender branches, was naked. In the basal part of the stem the stele had many arms and a pith; pith is lacking in upper, more slender regions.

Although the Rhynie chert flora is perhaps the best known Devonian assemblage of simple vascular plants, many other significant collections have been made of psilophytic plants, some of them from strata much older than those of the Scottish localities. In fact, Silurian psilophytes are known from Australia, and Lower Devonian members have been found in continental Europe, Great Britain, North America, and Australia.

The British *Cooksonia* resembles *Rhynia* in many respects. It is known from slender, naked, dichotomously branched stem fragments that were terminated by simple sporangia. Its age is thought to be Upper Silurian or Lower Devonian.

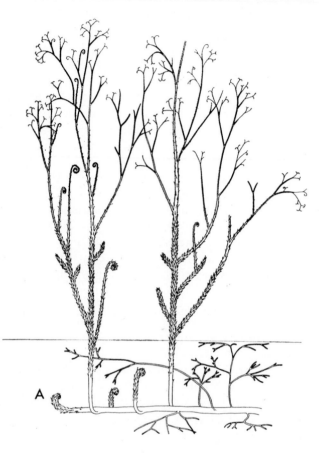

A

Another Silurian plant, this one from Australia, is *Hedeia,* which is also known from fragments. It appears to have terminated in a compact, three-dimensional branching system with sporangia at the tips of many of the branches.

The Australian *Yarravia,* also Silurian in age, has naked axes 2 mm wide terminated by large synangia, about 9 by 4 to 5 mm, composed of a small number of elongated sporangia (Fig. 4-1C).

Zosterophyllum, known from both the Upper Silurian and Lower Devonian, had a dichotomously branched vegetative system from which arose fertile axes. Fertile branches had closely spaced sporangia in a spikelike arrangement; the sporangia may have had

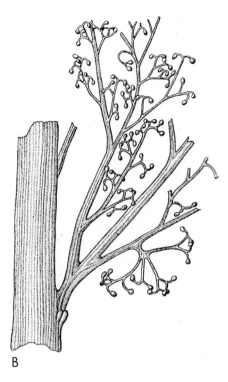

Fig. 4-2. A, (opposite) reconstruction of *Asteroxylon elberfeldense,* a Middle Devonian psilophyte from Germany. (Redrawn from Kräusel and Weyland, 1926.) B, (right) *Paulophyton Jongmansi,* a psilophyte-like plant from the Carboniferous. (Redrawn from Kräusel, 1957.)

B

short stalks. The lower, vegetative portion was somewhat unusual in that angles formed at the various regions of dichotomy were quite variable, and in many cases some of the branches are directed back toward the parent axis. A strand of annular tracheids traverses each of the axes.

Bucheria, a Lower Devonian plant from Wyoming, is incompletely known, but it has spikelike clusters of sporangia like those in *Zosterophyllum. Pectinophyton,* which originated in Lower Devonian rocks of western Siberia, is known from fragments with lateral branches bearing clusters of sporangia that are aggregated into spikelike groups. Each sporangium is flattened, and the stalk is recurved around part of the sporangium.

The Lower Devonian *Taeniocrada* has a flattened, dichotomously branched, thalluslike body, and one species has terminal sporangia.

Paulophyton is a Carboniferous psilophyte genus with a prominent main axis and much-branched lateral members. Some of the ultimate segments terminated in ellipsoidal sporangia (Fig. 4-2B).

There are still many other kinds of early plants, many of them psilophytic, others less well identifiable as to group, found in Devonian or older rocks. It will be apparent that many of these forms cannot justifiably be placed in the Psilophytales. If the criterion of sporangia terminating certain branches is applied to delimit the Psilophytales, then forms like *Zosterophyllum, Bucheria, Pectinophyton,* and many others would fail to fulfill the necessary requirements. The exact position of such plants in present systems of classification is yet to be determined. Perhaps the difficulty in classifying these plants and determining their relationships is due to the practice of instituting what actually are manmade categories and then attempting to force into them certain groups of organisms that refuse to conform.

It is of no great concern, however, that many of these early Paleozoic plants are not identifiable as members of any of the presently known groups of land plants. What is important about these plants is their generally simple nature and apparently primitive structure. They represent types that are about as simple as one could conceive a vascular plant to be. Many are undoubtedly members of orders or even larger categories that are now completely extinct. They might best be regarded, then, as an extremely plastic group of plants representing a wide assortment of "experimental stages" in the evolution of the plant kingdom. Some were successful in their competition with elements involved in a land existence; others were less well adapted and left no descendants.

To those who believe that all known organisms should be classified, it may seem unorthodox not to attempt to categorize these Silurian and Devonian plants. On the other hand, those familiar with the fossil record realize the impossibility of placing some of these forms into presently accepted taxa, or, which might confuse matters further, of establishing new taxa for them. It is likely that with more paleobotanical research more taxa of the rank of order or even higher will have to be introduced; with the present fund of knowledge, however, it is best to proceed cautiously along these lines. Even when well-defined groups become recognized, there will be many forms that will show characteristics transitional between taxa.

Perhaps the real significance of paleobotanical investigations that elucidate the structure of simple early Paleozoic plants lies in the fact that without the fossil record, we would almost be unaware of the existence of such a group of Tracheophyta as the Psilophytales. It is true that the extant *Psilotum* and *Tmesipteris* are relatively simple and may possibly show affinities with the extinct group, but on the other hand, there are some botanists who would regard the peculiar contemporary genera as being specialized through reduction. Whether or not the Psilophytales gave rise to other groups of land plants may not be proved in the immediate future. But the Silurian and Devonian rocks show that the so-called "psilophytic habit" was a predominant one, and it would certainly be within the realm of possibility for some of these plants to have served as the prototypes of later, more complex groups.

REFERENCES

ANANIEV, A. R., 1957. "New plant fossils from the Lower Devonian of Torgachino in the southeastern part of West Siberia," *Botan. Zhur. S.S.S.R.*, **42**: 691–702.

ANDREWS, H. N., JR., 1959. "Evolutionary trends in early vascular plants," *Cold Spring Harbor Symposia*, **24**: 217–234.

AXELROD, D. I., 1959. "Evolution of the psilophyte paleoflora," *Evolution*, **13**: 264–275.

COOKSON, ISABEL C., 1935. "On plant remains from the Silurian of Victoria, Australia, that extend and connect floras hitherto described," *Phil. Trans. Roy. Soc. London*, **225B**: 127–148.

———, 1949. "Yeringian (Lower Devonian) plant remains from Lilydale, Victoria, with notes on a collection from a locality in the Siluro-Devonian sequence," *Mem. Nat. Mus.* Melbourne, **16**: 117–130.

DAWSON, J. W., 1859. "On fossil plants from the Devonian rocks of Canada," *Quart. J. Geo. Soc. London*, **15**: 477–488.

DORF, E., 1933. "A new occurrence of the oldest known terrestrial vegetation from Beartooth Butte, Wyoming," *Botan. Gaz.*, **95**: 240–256.

KIDSTON, R., and W. H. LANG, 1917. "On Old Red Sandstone plants showing structure, from the Rhynie chert bed, Aberdeenshire. Part I. *Rhynia Gwynne-Vaughani* Kidston and Lang," *Trans. Roy. Soc. Edinburgh*, **51**: 761–784.

———, 1920. *Ibid.*, "Part II. Additional notes on *Rhynia Gwynne-Vaughani*, Kidston and Lang; with descriptions of *Rhynia major* n. sp., and *Hornea Lignieri*, n. g., n. sp.," *Trans. Roy. Soc. Edinburgh*, **52**: 603–627.

———, 1920. *Ibid.*, "Part III. *Asteroxylon Mackiei*, Kidston and Lang," *Trans. Roy. Soc. Edinburgh*, **52**: 643–680.

KIDSTON, R., and W. H. LANG, 1921. *Ibid.*, "Part IV. Restorations of the vascular cryptogams, and discussion of their bearing on the general morphology of the Pteridophyta and the origin of the organisation of land-plants," *Trans. Roy. Soc. Edinburgh*, **52**: 831–854.

―――, 1921. *Ibid.*, "Part V. The Thallophyta occurring in the peat-bed; the succession of the plants throughout a vertical section of the bed, and the conditions of accumulation and preservation of the deposit," *Trans. Roy. Soc. Edinburgh*, **52**: 855–902.

KRÄUSEL, R., 1957. "*Paulophyton jongmansi* n. sp. eine Pflanze altertümlichen Baues aus dem Namur des Ruhrgebietes," *Mededel. Geol. Stichting*, n. s., **11**: 21–25.

―――, and H. WEYLAND, 1926. "Beiträge zur Kenntnis der Devonflora II," *Abh. Senckenberg. naturforsch., Ges.*, **40**: 113–155.

―――, 1930. "Die Flora des Deutschen Unterdevons," *Abhandl. Preuss. Geol. Landes.*, **131**: 1–92.

KRISHTOFOVICH, A. N., 1953. "Discovery of lycopodiaceous plants in the east Siberian Cambrian," *Doklady Akad. Nauk S.S.S.R.*, **91**: 1377–1379.

LANG, W. H., 1937. "On the plant remains of the Downtonian of England and Wales," *Phil. Trans. Roy. Soc. London*, **227B**: 245–291.

―――, and ISABEL C. COOKSON, 1930. "Some fossil plants of early Devonian type from the Walhalla Series, Victoria, Australia," *Phil. Trans. Roy. Soc. London*, **219B**: 133–163.

―――, 1935. "On a flora, including vascular land plants associated with *Monograptus*, in rocks of Silurian age, from Victoria, Australia," *Phil. Trans. Roy. Soc. London*, **224B**: 421–449.

LECLERCQ, SUZANNE, 1954. "Are the Psilophytales a starting or a resulting point?" *Svensk Botan. Tidskr.*, **48**: 301–315.

LIGNIER, O., 1903. "Equisétales et Sphénophyllales," *Bull. Soc. Linn. Normandie* ser. **5**, **7**: 93–137.

―――, 1908. "Sur l'évolution morphologique du règne végétal," *Assoc. franç. avance. sci.*, **1908**: 530–542.

STEWART, W. N., 1960. "More about the origin of vascular plants," *Plant Sci. Bull.*, **6** (5): 1–5.

TASCH, P., 1957. "Flora and fauna of the Rhynie chert: a paleoecological re-evaluation of published evidence," *Univ. Wichita Bull.*, **32** (1): 1–24.

ZIMMERMANN, W., 1952. "Main results of the telome theory," *Palaeobotanist*, **1**: 456–470.

―――, 1959. *Die Phylogenie der Pflanzen*, 2nd ed., Stuttgart: Gustav Fischer.

chapter five ▸ Subdivision Lycopsida

This group of tracheophytes has a history at least as long as that of the Psilopsida, perhaps even longer. In fact there has been one recent report of Cambrian lycopodlike plants, but the majority of paleobotanists discount the report as inconclusive. There are, however, Silurian and Lower Devonian plants that are unquestionably members of the Lycopsida and that have a more complicated organization than that of the Psilophytales.

In contrast to the generally leafless condition of the Psilopsida, members of the Lycopsida have true leaves. Roots serve as the anchoring and absorbing system, and they are generally adventitious. Sporangia are found on the adaxial side of the modified leaves or sporophylls, which are often congested on an axis into a cone or strobilus. Lycopsid leaves are generally spoken of as microphylls, not necessarily because of their size, but because of their probable origin from enations rather than from branch systems. This suggested source of microphylls is reflected in the anatomy of the stem: the stele has no gaps in the positions of origin of leaf traces. While it is true that most microphylls are diminutive, certain extant lycopsids (for example, *Isoetes*) have sizable leaves, and in some of the fossil forms leaves up to a meter in length are known.

The genera *Lycopodium, Phylloglossum, Selaginella, Isoetes,* and *Stylites* are the only remnants of the Lycopsida found at the present time. The group, however, has had a long history, and during some periods members of the Lycopsida were among the dominants of the forests. A number of interesting evolutionary series can be detected in the group as well.

33

A tentative classification of the subdivision follows:
Protolepidodendrales – Silurian to Devonian-Mississippian
Lepidodendrales – Devonian to Permian
Pleuromeiales – Triassic to Cretaceous
Isoetales – Cretaceous to present
Lycopodiales – Carboniferous to present
Selaginellales – Carboniferous to present

PROTOLEPIDODENDRALES

One of the earliest of the Paleozoic lycopsids is *Baragwanathia longifolia,* from the Upper Silurian of Australia (Fig. 5-3A). *Baragwanathia* and the genera immediately following in the discussion are often placed in the order Protolepidodendrales, which includes the oldest and most primitive of the Lycopsida. Although the material of *Baragwanathia* is primarily compression, a little of the anatomy is recognizable. Stems were covered with spirally arranged leaves 4 cm long and 1 mm wide, each with a single vein. The branches forked dichotomously and ranged from 1 to 6.5 cm in diameter. Reniform sporangia 2 mm wide, with spores 50μ in diameter were borne near the leaf axils. It cannot be determined with certainty whether the sporangia were actually on the upper surfaces of sporophylls or on the stems in the leaf axils. These apparently homosporous plants had a fluted xylem strand in the stem, and annular tracheids have been detected.

The Lower and Middle Devonian *Drepanophycus* is another lycopsid with a general structure not unlike that of *Lycopodium.* From horizontal, branched rhizomes arose upright axes. Leaves 1 to 2 cm long covered the aerial stems, which were 2 to 5 cm wide. Sporangia were adaxial on sporophylls.

Protolepidodendron, known from the Lower and Middle Devonian, also had branched, horizontal, leaf-covered stems (Fig. 5-1D). Upright branching stems arose from these and are characterized by spindle-shaped leaf bases, or cushions, on which the leaves themselves were borne. Leaves on the aerial stems were forked at the tip, and some of them bore ovoid sporangia on the upper surfaces. One species of *Protolepidodendron* has a three-lobed stele with scalariform tracheids.

New York State has been the source of a number of other

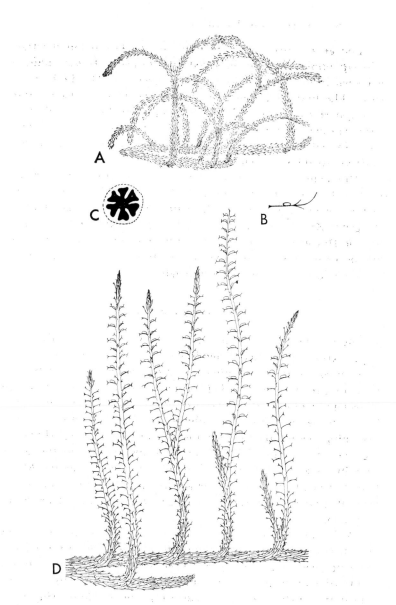

Fig. 5-1. A, reconstruction of *Colpodexylon Deatsii*, a Devonian lycopsid; B, sporophyll of *C. Deatsii* with adaxial sporangium; C, transverse section of the stem with an exarch actinostele. (A–C, from Banks, 1960.) D, *Protolepidodendron Scharyanum*, reconstruction. (Redrawn from Kräusel and Weyland, 1932.)

35

lycopsid genera that can be included in the Protolepidodendrales. *Gilboaphyton* (sometimes included with the genus *Archaeosigillaria*) is known from compressions of stem fragments in Middle Devonian rocks. The branching stems are about 1 cm thick and have spirally arranged spiny leaves about 5 mm long. The Middle and Upper Devonian genus *Colpodexylon* is similar, but has low leaf cushions and 3-forked leaves (Fig. 5-1A, B). A lobed xylem strand has been observed in the stem (Fig. 5-1C).

One genus that has often been confused with *Protolepidodendron* is *Archaeosigillaria*, which extends from the Upper Devonian to the Lower Carboniferous. (If *Gilboaphyton* is included within the genus *Archaeosigillaria*, then the range is extended back to the Middle Devonian.) Small leaves on this branched plant were borne on fusiform, or sometimes hexagonal, leaf bases. One species, *A. primaeva*, grew up to 5 meters in height.

LEPIDODENDRALES

By far the most conspicuous and striking group of Lycopsida is the extinct order Lepidodendrales, which includes some of the giant trees of the Carboniferous. What might be considered a typical representative, *Lepidodendron* probably attained a height of 30 meters or more, with a diameter of 2 meters near the base (Fig. 5-2). The large trunk was unbranched for some distance; first branchings were generally dichotomous, with more unequal branching toward the tips of the crown branches. Leaves in the crown were linear and variable in size among the various species. At the base of the plant, in the underground portion, there was also a branching system with spirally arranged, rootlike appendages borne on the axes.

Although remains of arborescent lycopsids are extremely abundant in late Paleozoic deposits, the growth habit of these plants has long been a puzzle. Latest work seems to indicate that the trunks of mature plants were unbranched for some distance and were limited externally by a massive layer of periderm. Higher up in the trunk were persistent leaf bases that have a characteristic diamond shape in *Lepidodendron* (Fig. 5-3B). These leaf bases are actually elevated cushions, and the leaf itself was borne at the apex of the pyramidlike structure about one third of the distance from

Fig. 5-2. Reconstruction of a plant of the genus *Lepidodendron*. (From Eggert, 1961.)

Fig. 5-3. A, fragment of *Baragwanathia longifolia*, an Upper Silurian lycopsid from Australia. (From Lang and Cookson, 1935.) B, impression of the trunk of *Lepidodendron obovatum* showing a region with leaf bases grading into one limited externally by periderm. C, fragment of *Lepidodendron Haidingeri* showing branching and decrease in leaf size distally. D, tangential section of the leaf bases of a petrified specimen of *Lepidophloios kansanus*. E, impression of the stem surface of *Sigillaria* cf. *mamillaris* with numerous, helically arranged leaf bases. F, transverse section of xylem and pith of *Sigillaria approximata*. (From Delevoryas, 1957.) G, cross section of *Paurodendron radiatum*, a Carboniferous herbaceous lycopsid, at a level just below a branch separation.

the tip of the rhombus. The position of the leaf is marked by a leaf scar, and within the leaf scar can be seen a leaf trace scar with a small mark on either side of it. These additional scars represent strands of loosely arranged parenchyma, often given the name parichnos. Just below the leaf scar are two additional parichnos scars.

Higher up, the main axis branched, and each member is smaller than the parent axis and has fewer rows of leaves, as well as somewhat smaller leaf bases. Successive branchings resulted in smaller and smaller axes (Fig. 5-3C). The smaller sizes of these axes are not only a function of immaturity, but they actually had less potential for growth than did more nearly basal branches. Leaf bases are progressively smaller and there are fewer rows of leaves as one approaches the tip. Furthermore, leaves may be found attached to leaf cushions in the crown branches, and it is evident that leaves of more distal branches are smaller than those on lower axes.

Internally there is also a progressive change in structure from base to apex. In the main trunk, near the base, there was probably a protostele with a tiny primary xylem strand and considerable secondary xylem. Higher up in the main axis, the primary xylem strand became medullated and grew progressively larger. Secondary xylem is less well developed higher up than it is nearer the base. Probably the maximum stelar size was attained just below the level of the first dichotomy, above which the daughter axes had steles with smaller primary dimensions than were found in the main axis just below. Subsequent branchings resulted in smaller steles, with smaller primary xylem cylinders, less secondary xylem, and eventually a complete absence of pith. It cannot be argued that the tiny protostelic axes at the tips of the crown system were simply immature and that with subsequent development they would have become more similar to larger axes. It would not be possible for a small protostele with a small number of tiny tracheids to mature into a siphonostele with many large primary tracheids. Furthermore, there is no way for the numbers of rows of leaves to increase or for the leaf bases to become larger, both longitudinally and laterally. Thus it appears as if the growth habit of these ar- borescent lycopsids was limited — the plant literally "used itself up" as it continued to branch. This type of growth habit may seem a

little hard to comprehend or to believe, but it really is not un-
heard of among modern plants. Certain species of *Lycopodium* have
a similar growth habit in the lateral axes. *Equisetum,* too, shows a
limited pattern of growth; lateral axes are smaller, with fewer appendages, than parent axes.

Steles of *Lepidodendron* are exarch, and tracheids are characterized by scalariform secondary thickenings. Characteristic of these
scalariform tracheids are delicate, threadlike structures on the pit
membrane joining adjacent scalariform bars. While not unique
among the arborescent Lycopsida, these fimbrils are consistent in
the group. Nothing comparable to secondary phloem was produced
in *Lepidodendron* steles.

Surrounding the stele is an extensive cortex that was the site
of abundant periderm formation as the tree matured. Certain of
the cells in the cortex beneath the leaf bases began to undergo
a series of periclinal divisions to produce a mass of radially aligned,
peridermlike cells. This tissue was probably not like cork; it appears
as if the cells remained living for some time and retained the power
to divide. As the periderm became thicker, splits developed between
leaf bases, and eventually the leaf bases, which consisted mostly of
primary tissues, dropped off. It seems unlikely that leaf bases extended to the very base of old plants, as is shown in some well-
known reconstructions (note Fig. 5-3B). Although a *Lepidodendron*
trunk may have attained a massive diameter, the stele never got to
be proportionately as large. The bulk of the large basal portions
of stems was largely a result of a tremendous amount of periderm
formation.

A similar pattern of development can be found in the underground portions of these plants; the name assigned to them is
Stigmaria. Two closely spaced dichotomies occurred at the base
of the upright trunk, resulting in a system with four main axes. Each
of these axes continued to divide, each daughter branch having a
smaller stele than the parent axis. Steles of these underground axes
were not quite like those of aerial stems; a pith is usually found
in them (except in small, distal axes), and the primary xylem is
indistinct. It is thought that the primary xylem is endarch in at
least some forms.

From these underground, branching stigmarian axes arise
spirally arranged, rootlike appendages, the morphology of which has

posed some interesting questions. First, the arrangement of these appendages is spiral, unlike any typical root arrangement. Furthermore, the vascular bundle of an appendage is bilaterally symmetrical (a monarch bundle), again differing from radially oriented root vascular systems (although distal rootlets of certain plants have monarch bundles). Finally, the origin of these rootlike structures is close to the surface of the parent axis and not completely endogenous as are typical lateral roots. Thus it is understandable why some workers choose to call these appendages homologues of leaves (leaves are often spirally arranged, have collateral bundles, and are exogenous) that have been modified for an anchoring and absorptive function.

The name *Lepidophyllum* has for some time been applied to leaves of many of the arborescent lycopsids, but because the name has priority in use for a flowering plant, it is not applicable to the vascular cryptogams. These leaves ranged in size from a few millimeters to over a meter. There probably was a considerable range in size on one tree, but it is also likely that different species could have had different size ranges. A single vascular bundle extends through the length of the leaf, and on either side are two dorsal furrows in which the stomata are placed.

Cones (genus *Lepidostrobus*) that were terminal on some of the smaller branches had spirally arranged (sometimes whorled) sporophylls, and it is generally believed that they were heterosporous. Some cones have both microsporophylls and megasporophylls on the same axis. A sporophyll bears a sporangium on the upper, or adaxial, surface, and beyond the sporangium the sporophyll bends upward abruptly. Often there is an abaxial, heellike projection at the position of bending. A fleshy, sterile outgrowth of the sporophyll sometimes extends into the sporangium. In many forms a ligule is present on the upper surface of the sporophyll just beyond the position of attachment of the sporangium.

Externally, cones show spirally arranged distal tips of sporophylls that overlap sporophylls of higher nodes.

Spores of arborescent lycopsid cones characteristically have prominent three-rayed marks that are the result of close appression of spores in quartets. Sculpturing on the exines is variable among various lycopsid spore genera, and spores may be further elaborated with complicated flanges or other projections. Lycopsid spores are

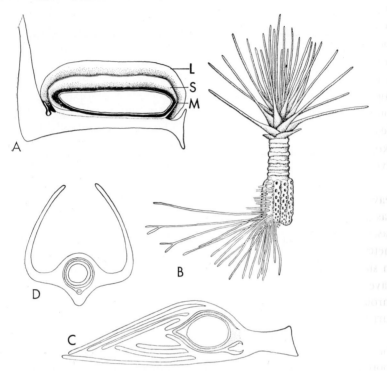

Fig. 5-4. A, diagrammatic reconstruction of *Lepidocarpon* cut longitudinally. L—lateral lamina, S—sporangium, M—megaspore. (Slightly modified from Hoskins and Cross, 1941.) B, reconstruction of *Nathorstiana arborea*, a Cretaceous lycopsid. (Redrawn from Mägdefrau, 1932.) C, longitudinal section of *Miadesmia membranacea*, a Carboniferous lycopsid seedlike body with a single megaspore contained within a sporangium enveloped by a fringed sporophyll. D, transverse section of *Miadesmia membranacea*. (C and D redrawn from Benson, 1908.)

abundant in Carboniferous coals, and the fact that some species of *Lepidostrobus* attained a length of three fourths of a meter is sufficient to give some idea of the profusion of spores that must have loaded the air during the Carboniferous period.

A morphological characteristic of some arborescent lycopsid cones sheds some light on the problem of understanding the origin of seeds. Many species of *Lepidostrobus* have a large number of megaspores in a megasporangium. Other fossil lycopsid cones have a much smaller number, only four, for example, in some cases. The genus *Lepidocarpon* shows a further reduction in megaspore number, with only one functional megaspore in a sporangium (Fig. 5-4A). It is often possible to see the three aborted spores that were part of the spore quartet produced as a result of meiosis of a single spore mother cell. The functional megaspore is quite large at maturity, practically filling the sporangium. In well-preserved megaspores it is possible to see megagametophyte cells with well-developed archegonia. Another modification in *Lepidocarpon* involves the sporophyll itself. Two lateral laminae of the sporophyll almost completely envelop the sporangium, leaving an open slit at the top. Thus one sporophyll of *Lepidocarpon,* with its sporangium, megaspore, and megagametophyte, has many similarities to a gymnosperm ovule. The enveloping megasporophyll might be compared with the integument; the sporangium is homologous with the megasporangium or nucellus of a gymnosperm; and the gametophytes are alike in many respects. This is not to imply that seeds of seed plants have any connection with lycopsid "seeds," but the parallel is too striking to be ignored. It is likely that a similar series might have been involved in the origin of a gymnosperm ovule, starting with a sporangium with many megaspores and ending with an integumented nucellus having a single functional spore. In *Lepidocarpon* the sporangium actually dehisced; thus it might be argued that, strictly speaking, a sporophyll of this genus cannot be considered a seed.

Other genera of arborescent Lycopsida are known from Carboniferous deposits, some varying from *Lepidodendron* only in particulars. *Lepidophloios* was also a branched form that differed from *Lepidodendron* primarily in its leaf-base characteristics. In *Lepidopholoios,* leaf bases present a flattened rhombic pattern, with the horizontal axis of each base longer than the vertical one (Fig. 5-3D). In addition, the leaf bases actually overlapped, like shingles on a roof. The position of the leaf on the base is marked by a leaf scar at the lower edge of the base. Leaves bent up abruptly from the bases, and a leaf scar left by a fallen leaf shows the same marks exhibited by a *Lepidodendron* leaf scar. Above the leaf scar on the leaf base is the ligule. Whereas in *Lepidodendron* cones were thought to terminate small apical branches, cones of *Lepidophloios* were probably borne on short lateral branches. Prominent scars left on trunks of *Lepidophloios* are interpreted by some workers to represent scars left after abscission of the specialized fertile axes.

Bothrodendron is another closely related genus that usually lacks leaf bases (occasionally not very pronounced bases are present) and that has leaf scars on what appears to be a smooth trunk surface. Above the leaf scar in compression specimens can be seen a small ligule scar.

Cones generally assignable to *Bothrodendron* are not unlike those of the extant *Selaginella*. Four very thick-walled megaspores were produced in a sporangium, and well-preserved remains of gametophytes with archegonia have been observed.

Levicaulis arranensis, from the Lower Carboniferous of Scotland, is a protostelic lycopsid resembling *Bothrodendron* in many ways. It differs, however, in the complete absence of leaf bases, even on the smallest axes, whereas small twigs of *Bothrodendron* may have small bases.

Very common as compressions and impressions, but rather rare in the petrified state, are stems of the genus *Sigillaria*. This Carboniferous and Permian genus is characterized by an unbranched or sparsely branched habit, a terminal crown of grasslike leaves, and characteristic leaf bases. These bases, although actually spirally arranged, appear to be in vertical rows (Fig. 5-3E). The illusion of vertical rows is further enhanced in some species by the presence of vertical ribs of the stem surface on which the leaves were borne. A leaf scar may be flattened hexagonally or extended laterally to resemble the outline of a pair of lips. Each scar has a leaf-trace scar and two parichnos scars, as in other arborescent lycopsid genera. A system of classification of *Sigillaria* stems has been established, based on the presence or absence of ribs and closeness of scars. Because many specimens are known to intergrade between one kind and another, the validity of such a classification may be questioned.

Internally, sigillarian axes are siphonostelic, with the primary xylem usually in a continuous cylinder around a rather large pith (Fig. 5-3F). The primary xylem has a sinuous outline in cross section, and leaf traces arise from the furrows of the primary xylem. Protoxylem is outermost. Secondary xylem is often found in *Sigillaria* steles, and tracheids show the characteristic scalariform thickening, with fimbrils extending between adjacent scalariform bars.

Periderm development appears to have been the same as in *Lepidodendron*, and it is not uncommon to find bulky masses of petrified sigillarian periderm in some American coal ball localities.

Parichnos strands accompany leaf traces through the cortex and periderm, and often in thick petrified slabs of sigillarian periderm one may see the parichnos strands and leaf traces, both of which apparently had the ability to increase in length as the stem grew in diameter.

Sigillaria leaves are much like those of *Lepidodendron*, although the abaxial furrows in the former are considerably more pronounced and may be lined with conspicuous hairs. Sometimes leaves of *Sigillaria* have two vascular bundles.

Fructifications of *Sigillaria* were borne among the leaves and are of two types. *Sigillariostrobus* is much like *Lepidostrobus;* it is heterosporous and the sporophylls have conspicuously pointed tips.

Mazocarpon, also heterosporous, is better known. In *M. oedipternum,* a common Upper Pennsylvanian species from the United States, each sporophyll has a downwardly projecting, heel-like extension on the abaxial side where the distal lamina bends upward. Within the adaxial sporangium is a conspicuous mound of tissue that is surrounded by the sporogenous region. In microsporangia, many microspores are in the cavity between the pad of tissue and the sporangium wall; only eight saucer-shaped megaspores are in each megasporangium. On the concave, proximal face of the spore is a small triradiate mark. Portions of the megagametophyte, with structures resembling archegonia are visible.

Although the arborescent lycopsids reached their maximum development late in the Paleozoic era and had no counterparts in later times, it is possible to trace what appears to be a well-documented evolutionary series from the Lepidodendrales to the modern *Isoetes,* or quillwort.

PLEUROMEIALES

The genus *Pleuromeia*, Triassic in age, is the type of the order Pleuromeiales. *Pleuromeia* was unbranched, with an erect trunk a meter or more in height. The base of the trunk was marked with four or more bulky, upturned lobes on which were borne many spirally arranged rootlets. Just below the apex of the plant was a crown of elongated, tapering leaves, that left lip-shaped scars after dropping off. One large heterosporous terminal cone was produced. The position of the sporangium appears to have been abaxial, but this configuration may well be because the sporangia were actually adaxial but set deep within the sporophyll, thus causing a dorsal bulge (compare with *Isoetes* sporophylls). The rounded and concave sporophylls were arranged spirally.

There is not actually too great a step from an unbranched arborescent lycopsid like *Sigillaria* to the much smaller and later *Pleuromeia*. The four or so lobes at the base of a *Pleuromeia* stem could be interpreted as stunted stigmarian axes, which, in *Sigillaria*, are usually arranged in a group of four at the stem base. The arrangement of *Pleuromeia* rootlets is like that in *Stigmaria*. Instead of many cones, only one is left in *Pleuromeia*.

The Cretaceous *Nathorstiana* is also often placed in the order Pleuromeiales. It was a diminutive plant, about 20 cm tall, unbranched, and with several longitudinal basal ridges that bore spirally arranged roots (Fig. 5-4B). At the apex of the short stem was a crown of slender leaves. Unfortunately, nothing is known of the sporophylls. *Nathorstiana* might be regarded as representing a plant even more reduced than *Pleuromeia* and, in general habit, approaching *Isoetes*.

ISOETALES

Indeed, *Isoetes*-like plants have been found in Cretaceous deposits and are often called *Isoetites*. The modern *Isoetes* has a cormlike stem with two lobes, and a meristem at each end. At the upper end is a crown of long, grasslike leaves, while spirally oriented rootlets are borne on the lower portion. Some of the leaves are fertile, with deeply embedded adaxial sporangia.

It might be possible, then, to interpret *Isoetes* as the end member of a long evolutionary series that began with unbranched, heterosporous, arborescent lycopsids. Some of the modifications involved a shortening of the stigmarian system, a reduction in the number of cones, and a telescoping or shortening of the stem. *Pleuromeia* shows the first stage in such a series; *Nathorstiana* is even more reduced; and *Isoetes* is little more than a heterosporous cone seated on a stunted stigmarian base. Anatomy of *Isoetes* rootlets is amazingly similar to that of stigmarian rootlets. From the foregoing statements it should not be inferred that *Sigillaria* is the direct ancestor of *Isoetes*, with *Pleuromeia* and *Nathorstiana* representing members on a direct line to *Isoetes*. They should be regarded, rather, as representing varying degrees of reduction and hinting as to what might have been the series of evolutionary modifications leading to the peculiar *Isoetes*.

While it is conceivable that *Isoetes* and the closely related South American genus *Stylites* may be descendants of a line of arborescent lycopsids, the other extant herbaceous lycopsids have a distinct history and are probably descendants of ancestors that may never have been arborescent.

LYCOPODIALES

The order Lycopodiales was probably derived from some of the smaller forms in the Protolepidodendrales and was recognizable in the Carboniferous. In fact, the late Paleozoic genus *Lycopodites* looks similar to the modern *Lycopodium Selago*.

Paurodendron is a petrified Carboniferous genus thought to have been lycopodiaceous (Fig. 5-3G). The slender stem, which is just a few millimeters in diameter, may have no appendages along part of its length, while elsewhere there may be many slender, spirally arranged microphylls. In its general habit *Paurodendron* resembles a modern *Lycopodium,* except that ligules have been reported in the fossil genus. No fructifications are known on this plant. Internally there is a protostele with several projecting protoxylem points. Fimbrils, like those found on tracheids of arborescent Lycopsida, are present on the tracheid walls of *Paurodendron*.

SELAGINELLALES

The order Selaginellales is also known in the Carboniferous, and *Selaginellites* is one common example. It is frequently found as a compression fossil, and the anisophyllous character is recognizable even there. Cones assignable to *Selaginellites* are known in the petrified state. The sporophyll structure and organization of these heterosporous cones are very much like those in *Selaginella*.

There are generally four thick-walled megaspores in a mega-sporangium; many microspores fill the microsporangia. A ligule is present on the sporophyll as in *Selaginella.*

A Lower Carboniferous genus sometimes assigned to the Selaginellales, but whose exact affinities are still uncertain, is *Miadesmia,* which represents a curious parallel to *Lepidocarpon* (Fig. 5-4C, D). As in *Lepidocarpon,* there is but one functional megaspore in the sporangium, and the sporophyll is elaborately extended about the sporangium, resembling very closely a winged integument. The sporophyll margins are somewhat fringed, and a ligule is present on the sporophyll next to the sporangium. Only detached sporophylls are known, and it has been suggested that the plant that bore them might have been an herbaceous form.

From the foregoing treatment of the fossil Lycopsida, it at once becomes apparent that the group had a long and varied history. It reached its maximum development during the late Paleozoic, and since then the group has gradually become less significant and today is represented by only five genera. While many of the Carboniferous and Permian forms were massive arborescent plants, only herbaceous (*Selaginella* may sometimes appear "shrubby") members exist at the present time.

During the evolutionary history of the Lycopsida, several trends are evident. The general habit of the plant was typically a dichotomous system among the earliest types; later forms were monopodial and sympodial. Other forms remained unbranched.

Earliest lycopsids were protostelic; later arborescent types showed a "mixed pith" (protostele, with a large amount of parenchyma in the central portion). Still others had developed true siphonosteles (*Sigillaria,* some lepidodendra). No leaf gaps ever developed in the siphonostelic types, however.

With regard to spore types, there had been a general trend from homospory, to heterospory, to an extreme heterosporous condition such as that in *Lepidocarpon* and *Miadesmia* in which there is only one functional megaspore in each megasporangium and the lateral laminae of the sporophylls are modified into enveloping, integumentlike structures. The seed habit is closely mimicked. Along with spore differentiation occurred a specialization of sporophylls. Sporophylls of some of the earliest forms were little differentiated from vegetative leaves, while certain Carboniferous and Permian sporophylls were extremely modified, some into elaborate enveloping structures.

A trend in tracheid evolution is also evident. Earliest lycopsids had annular secondary wall thickenings, while later forms were predominantly scalariform.

Contrary to what some earlier paleobotanists may have believed, it is generally agreed that the Lycopsida gave rise to no other group of vascular plants.

REFERENCES

Amstutz, Erika, 1957. "*Stylites,* a new genus of Isoetaceae," *Ann. Missouri Botan. Gard.,* **44:** 121–123.

Andrews, H. N., and W. H. Murdy, 1958. "*Lepidophloios* — and ontogeny in arborescent lycopods," *Amer. J. Botan.,* **45:** 552–560.

Arnold, C. A., 1960. "A lepidodendrid stem from Kansas and its bearing on the problem of cambium and phloem in Paleozoic lycopods," *Univ. Michigan Contr. Mus. Paleont.,* **15:** 249–267.

Banks, H. P., 1944. "A new Devonian lycopod genus from southeastern New York," *Amer. J. Botan.,* **31:** 650–659.

———, 1960. "Notes on Devonian lycopods," *Senckenbergiana,* **41:** 59–88.

Barghoorn, E. S., and R. A. Scott, 1958. "Degradation of the plant cell wall and its relation to certain tracheary features of the Lepidodendrales," *Amer. J. Botan.,* **45:** 222–227.

Beck, C. B., 1958. "*Levicaulis arranensis,* gen. et sp. nov., a lycopsid axis from the Lower Carboniferous of Scotland," *Trans. Roy. Soc. Edinburgh,* **58:** 445–457.

Benson, Margaret, 1908. "*Miadesmia membranacea,* Bertrand; a new Palaeozoic lycopod with a seed-like structure," *Phil. Trans. Roy. Soc. London,* **199B:** 409–425.

Brown, R. W., 1939. "Some American fossil plants belonging to the Isoetales," *J. Wash. Acad. Sci.,* **29:** 261–269.

Delevoryas, T., 1957. "Anatomy of *Sigillaria approximata,*" *Amer. J. Botan.,* **44:** 654–660.

Eggert, D. A., 1961. "The ontogeny of Carboniferous arborescent Lycopsida," *Palaeontographica,* **108B:** 43–92.

Felix, C. J., 1952. "A study of the arborescent lycopods of southeastern Kansas," *Ann. Missouri Botan. Gard.,* **39:** 263–288.

———, 1954. "Some American arborescent lycopod fructifications," *Ann. Missouri Botan. Gard.,* **41:** 351–394.

Fry, W. L., 1954. "A study of the Carboniferous lycopod, *Paurodendron,* gen. nov.," *Amer. J. Botan.,* **41:** 415–428.

Hoskins, J. H., and Maxine L. Abbott, 1956. "*Selaginellites crassicinctus,* a new species from the Desmoinesian series of Kansas," *Amer. J. Botan.,* **43:** 36–46.

———, and A. T. Cross, 1941. "A consideration of the structure of *Lepidocarpon* Scott based on a new strobilus from Iowa," *Amer. Midl. Nat.,* **25:** 523–547.

Kräusel, R., and H. Weyland, 1932. "Pflanzenreste aus dem Devon. IV.— *Protolepidodendron* Krejci," *Senckenbergiana,* **14:** 391–403.

———, 1935. "Neue Pflanzenfunde im Rheinischen Unterdevon," *Palaeontographica,* **80B:** 171–190.

Krishtofovich, A. N., 1953. "Discovery of lycopodiaceous plants in the east Siberian Cambrian," *Doklady Akad. Nauk S.S.S.R.,* **91:** 1377–1379.

Lang, W. H., and Isabel C. Cookson, 1935. "On a flora, including vascular land plants, associated with *Monograptus,* in rocks of Silurian age, from Victoria, Australia," *Phil. Trans. Roy. Soc. London,* **224B:** 421–449.

Leisman, G. A., 1961. "Further observations on the structure of *Selaginellites crassicinctus,*" *Amer. J. Botan.,* **48:** 224–229.

Lundblad, Britta, 1948. "A selaginelloid strobilus from East Greenland (Triassic)," *Medd. Dansk Geol. Foren.,* **11:** 351–358.

Mägdefrau, K., 1931. "Zur Morphologie und phylogenetischen Bedeutung der fossilen Pflanzengattung *Pleuromeia,*" *Beih. Bot. Cbl.,* **48:** 119–140.

———, 1932. "Über *Nathorstiana,* eine Isoëtacee aus dem Neokom von Quedlinburg a. Harz." *Beih. Bot. Cbl.,* **49:** 706–718.

———, 1956. *Paläobiologie der Pflanzen,* 3rd ed., Jena: Gustav Fischer.

Schopf, J. M., 1941. "Contributions to Pennsylvanian paleobotany, *Mazocarpon oedipternum,* sp. nov., and sigillarian relationships," *Illinois Geol. Surv. Rep. Invest.,* **75:** 1–53.

Scott, D. H., 1901. "On the structure and affinities of fossil plants from the Palaeozoic rocks. IV. The seed-like fructification of *Lepidocarpon,* a genus of lycopodiaceous cones from the Carboniferous formation," *Phil. Trans. Roy. Soc. London,* **194:** 291–333.

Stewart, W. N., 1947. "A comparative study of stigmarian appendages and *Isoetes* roots," *Amer. J. Botan.,* **34:** 315–324.

———, 1960. "More about the origin of vascular plants," *Plant. Sci. Bull.,* **6** (5): 1–5.

Williamson, W. C., 1887. "A monograph of the morphology and histology of *Stigmaria ficoides,*" *Paleont. Soc. London.*

Wood, J. M., 1957. "The morphology and relationships of sigillarian fructifications from the Lower Pennsylvanian of Indiana," *Amer. Midl. Nat.,* **58:** 141–154.

chapter six ❯ Subdivision
Sphenopsida

In many respects the evolutionary history of the subdivision Sphenopsida parallels that of the Lycopsida. The sphenopsids had their origin early in the Paleozoic (the first ones are Lower Devonian), reached maximum development late in the Paleozoic, when they formed a conspicuous part of the vegetation, and have progressively dwindled to the present day. Only one genus, *Equisetum,* survives.

Like the Lycopsida, the Sphenopsida possess true roots, stems, and leaves. Generally the stems are articulated, and leaves and branches are borne in whorls at the nodes. Occasionally the stems are ribbed externally. Because of the unusual nature of the vascular system, it is difficult to determine with certainty whether leaf and branch gaps are present. It is probable that gaps are not left by departing leaf traces even though the leaves are thought to be modified branch systems. The branching systems of sphenopsid leaves, however, were not as extensive as those in the leaves of ferns and higher plants.

Another characteristic generally found among the sphenopsids is the presence of sporangium-bearing axes (sporangiophores) in whorls. In many forms, these sporangiophores are recurved, so that the terminal sporangia are directed toward the axis. Strobili are formed in many genera.

Commonly recognized orders of Sphenopsida are the following:
Hyeniales – Devonian

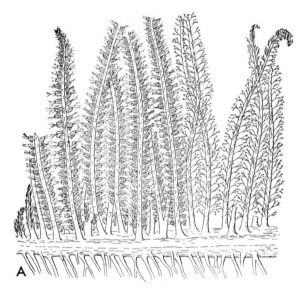

A

Pseudoborniales – Devonian
Calamitales – Upper Devonian to end of Paleozoic
Equisetales – Carboniferous to present
Sphenophyllales – Carboniferous to end of Paleozoic

Some of the earliest Sphenopsida are not classifiable into any of the recognized orders, but because of certain characteristics they are assigned to the subdivision. *Climaceophyton trifoliatum,* from the Lower Devonian of Germany, is represented by tiny fragments of a three-angled stem. In the space of a centimeter there are six whorls of rounded, leaflike appendages, three at a node.

The Lower Devonian *Sphondylophyton* was discovered in Wyoming and is known from unbranched stem fragments, some 3 cm in length, and about 1 to 2 mm thick. Two to four forked leaves were borne at nodes that were 4 to 6 mm apart; these appendages were 5 to 8 mm in length.

HYENIALES

Protohyenia is the oldest member of the Hyeniales; *P. Janovii* is known from Lower Devonian deposits of western Siberia. The

Fig. 6-1. A (opposite), reconstruction of a portion of *Hyenia elegans*, a Devonian sphenopsid.
(From Leclercq, 1940.) B, *Schizoneura paradoxa*,
reconstruction. (From Mägdefrau, 1956.)

B

stem fragments are unbranched and bear dichotomizing leaflike
appendages or, on some axes, dichotomizing lateral sporangiophores
with terminal sporangia. Although not too pronounced, there is a
hint of a whorled arrangement of the appendages. The reconstruction of *P. Janovii* shows several erect shoots originating from
a horizontal rhizomelike axis. It must be emphasized, however, that
this lower axis has never been seen.

The genus *Hyenia,* on the other hand, shows evidence of such
a horizontal rhizome (Fig. 6-1A). The Middle Devonian European
H. elegans had many upright, unbranched stems that bore whorls
of narrow, forked leaves 1 to 2.5 cm long. Other axes bore whorled,
dichotomously branched sporangiophores. Some of the ultimate portions of these lateral branched systems had inwardly directed
sporangia; sterile tips projected outward. Earlier reconstructions
pictured a digitately branched plant; the rhizomatous habit is a
more recent interpretation.

Calamophyton, a Middle Devonian genus of the Hyeniales, has a conspicuously articulated stem with a digitate branching pattern. *Calamophyton primaevum* (Fig. 6-2A), from Germany, has a stem up to 2 cm in diameter. Although the preservation is in

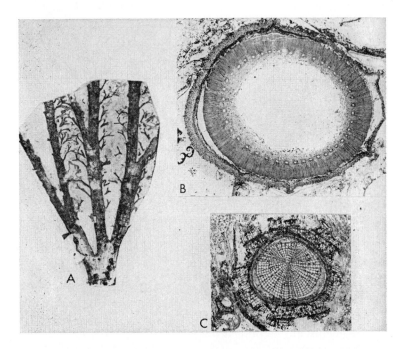

Fig. 6-2. A, fragment of *Calamophyton primaevum* from the Middle Devonian. On the branches are dichotomously forked leaves. (From Leclercq and Andrews, 1960.) B, transverse section of a small stem of *Arthropitys communis,* a Carboniferous calamitean genus. C, *Sphenophyllum plurifoliatum,* transverse section of a stem with secondary vascular tissues and periderm.

compression form, it was possible to detect reticulate and scalariform tracheids in the stem. From the digitate branches arise smaller, lateral axes in a monopodial fashion. Leaves were thought to have been notched and wedge-shaped, 8 to 10 mm long, but subsequent investigations demonstrated that they were actually three-dimensional, forking appendages. Some of the branches have a series of nodes with whorled, once-forked, and recurved sporangiophores, each usually with two sporangia.

The more recently investigated *C. bicephalum,* from Belgium, is better known and shows a high degree of complexity, especially in the fertile structures. The general branching habit of the plant is the same as in *C. primaevum.* Leaves seem to have been terete and forked one to four times to produce a three-dimensional photosynthetic system. Sporangiophores were also forked several times, and each sporangiophore had about 12 recurved sporangia and some outwardly directed sterile tips.

PSEUDOBORNIALES

The Upper Devonian Pseudoborniales is a little-known order, and is represented by the single species *Pseudobornia ursina,* from Bear Island, the southernmost island in the Svalbard Archipelago. Stout stem axes are found in the compressions, which may be up to 10 cm in diameter. There are also distinct nodes with prominent whorled appendages. At a node are about four leaves, each of which dichotomized two or three times near the point of attachment. The distal members of these leaves are feathery pinnate. Sporangia are borne in loose strobili up to 32 cm in length. Sporangiophores are whorled with sterile, bractlike portions and with sporangia borne on the lower surfaces.

CALAMITALES

Giant arborescent sphenopsids, so prominent in the Carboniferous, are included in the order Calamitales. This order is represented in the Upper Devonian and Lower Carboniferous by *Asterocalamites,* which had slender, whorled, dichotomously branched leaves up to 10 cm in length. Pith casts up to 16.5 cm in diameter are known. The inwardly projecting primary xylem groups are responsible for furrows in the casts, and the elevated ridges correspond to the rays between the bundles in the stem. Unlike many of the later members of the Calamitales, the ribs of one internode are superposed on those in the internode below. In the primary xylem are canals representing the former position of disintegrated protoxylem elements, much like the situation in the modern *Equisetum.* Secondary xylem was also present.

Pothocites is the name given to strobili thought to belong to

Asterocalamites. In general appearance these cones resemble those of *Equisetum;* whorls of sporangiophores with recurved sporangia are borne on the cone axis. There are no sterile bracts among the fertile appendages.

The petrified, Lower Carboniferous *Protocalamites* is typified by exarch primary xylem. *Mesocalamites,* most frequently found in the Upper Lower Carboniferous, has internodal bundles that are both superposed and alternated with bundles of internodes above and below.

Although originally established for pith casts, the name *Calamites* has developed broader connotations. Frequently an entire arborescent sphenopsid is referred to as *Calamites,* but other organ generic names are used for the various parts. Usual reconstructions represent calamites as having stout, horizontal, rhizomelike stems with adventitious roots arising from conspicuous nodes. From this horizontally growing axis arose upright, aerial shoot systems, and these, too, had conspicuous "jointed" stems with whorled leaf arrangement and paired or whorled branch placement. Three subgenera have been designated to represent different growth patterns. In the subgenus *Eucalamites* branches are borne at all, or nearly all, the nodes. Within this subgenus are forms with paired branches, while others have more than two per node. The subgenus *Calamitina* has nodes with branch whorls separated by a series of branchless nodes and internodes. *Stylocalamites* is a subgenus generally regarded as being entirely without branches, or having but a few major branch axes.

Calamitean leaves are usually assigned to one of two genera: *Annularia* and *Asterophyllites.* Leaves of *Annularia* are arranged in one plane at a node and are fused to each other at their bases. They are somewhat flattened dorsiventrally and each has a single vascular bundle. It is thought by some workers that the plane of the leaf whorl was not exactly perpendicular to the branch axis, a condition that would account for the fact that almost invariably, compressed specimens of *Annularia* show the leaf whorls flattened parallel with the bedding plane.

Asterophyllites is represented by narrower, more tapered leaves, which ascend from the node and which may overlap the leaves of the node above.

Sections of petrified calamitean stems (Fig. 6-2B) show a

hollow central pith region except at nodes, where diaphragms of pith are present. Surrounding the pith is the xylem, which may be massive in some cases. A number of endarch primary xylem bundles surround the pith, and each bundle has a hollow lacuna that represents the position of disintegration of first-formed protoxylem elements, a condition very similar to that in the extant *Equisetum.* Secondary xylem was formed centrifugally in wedge-shaped zones, separated by conspicuous vascular rays. Three genera of petrified calamitean stems are recognized on the basis of internal structure. In *Arthropitys* ray cells are horizontally oriented and are entirely parenchymatous. *Calamodendron* has large rays flanked on either side by fibrous elements. In *Arthroxylon,* the large rays between adjacent bundles consist of upright cells. Just how natural a separation of calamitean stem genera this is, is presently not known. Pitting in the secondary xylem ranges from scalariform bordered, through transitional, to circular bordered.

Although the xylem is in separate bundles in the internodal regions, at the nodes a continuous ring of xylem is present; leaf traces originate from this cylinder and leave no gaps. In pith casts the scars left by leaf traces can be seen at the lower ends of the ridges, while the upper ends of the ridges of the internode below have characteristic scars representing "infranodal canals," looser patches of tissue in the large rays.

The general growth pattern of calamitean stems resembles in many ways that of arborescent lycopsids. The underground rhizome and major stem axes had large piths, much secondary xylem, and a large number of primary xylem groups. Each successive order of branches showed smaller piths, less secondary xylem, and a smaller number of primary xylem groups (Fig. 6-3). It is conceivable that the diameter of the pith at a given level may have increased to some extent with age, but the number of primary xylem groups must have remained constant. Thus a small, more distal axis could never mature into a large axis such as is represented by a large trunk. A pattern typified by decreasing dimensions and a smaller number of bundles in more distal regions suggests, then, that calamitean stems had a determinate habit of growth, or at least one of progressive dwindling at distal regions. A twig of one of the ultimate branches could never look like the main stem, no matter how old it got to be, and some of the very tip branches

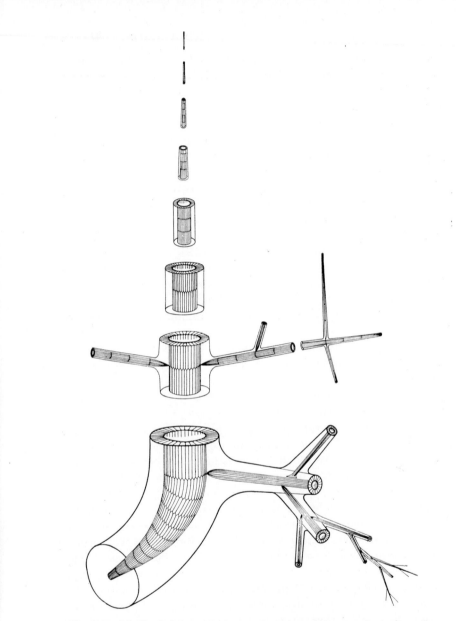

Fig. 6-3. Idealized diagrammatic representation of the vascular system of a typical calamitean plant showing progressive decrease in number of primary xylem bundles (striped areas) distally. Note also the smaller primary bodies in lateral branches of stems and roots. (From Eggert, 1962.)

are extremely tiny. It is interesting to note that *Equisetum* shows the same kind of determinate growth patern. More distal branches have smaller piths and fewer vascular bundles than do the larger axes.

Petrified calamitean roots are usually placed in the genus *Astromyelon*. In many respects they resemble stems, although no nodes and internodes are present, and primary xylem is exarch. Furthermore, there are no protoxylem lacunae in the primary xylem bundles. Another difference is that the wedges of xylem are somewhat less conspicuous in the roots than in the stems. *Astromyelon* appears to have been adventitious, arising from both the rhizomes and aerial stems.

Cones thought to have calamitean affinities are variable, but each has the characteristic whorled construction. *Calamostachys,* one of the more common petrified genera, has whorls of fertile appendages alternating with sterile bract whorls. The fertile sporangiophores arise approximately midway between adjacent sterile whorls. Sporangiophores are peltate, each with four sporangia directed toward the cone axis. Some species are definitely heterosporous, but in others only one kind of spore has been observed.

The general structure of the genus *Palaeostachya* is like that of *Calamostachys,* except that in the former the sporangiophores are borne closer to the sterile whorl below and are often ascending (Fig. 6-4A, B). Four recurved sporangia are present on each peltate sporangiophore. In some species of *Palaeostachya* the vascular bundles that supply the sporangiophores originate just above the node of sterile appendages, ascend, and then abruptly bend down again and enter the sporangiophore bases. This peculiar vascularization has led many to believe that although the sporangiophores are borne close to the sterile whorl below, the vascular pattern suggests that the ancestral types must have been like *Calamostachys,* in which the fertile whorls are borne approximately halfway between sterile whorls. A "phyletic slide" of the sporangiophore was supposed to have occurred, and the vascular pattern was somewhat delayed. Although this suggestion would seem to have considerable merit, complications in explaining sporangiophore position are found in at least one *Palaeostachya* in which the sporangiophore vascular bundles enter the sporangiophores directly, and in one species of *Calamostachys* in which sporangiophore traces ascend beyond the

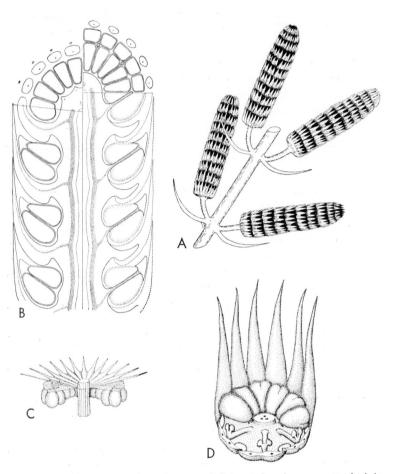

Fig. 6-4. A, reconstruction of cones of *Palaeostachya decacnema* attached in bract axils. B, idealized transverse and longitudinal sections of a portion of a cone of *P. decacnema*. The right part of the drawing is of a section through the sporangiophores, but not the sporangia; the left side has sectioned the sporangia, but not the sporangiophores. (A and B from Delevoryas, 1955.) C, diagrammatic reconstruction of part of a node of *Cingularia typica*. (Redrawn from Weiss, 1876.) D, reconstruction of a portion of a node of *Bowmanites bifurcatus* with some of the sporangia removed to show the branching sporangiophores. (Redrawn from Andrews and Mamay, 1951.)

point of attachment, bend down again, and enter the sporangiophores.

Mazostachys shows that sporangiophore position between adjacent sterile whorls may even be just below a sterile whorl. Each sporangiophore bears two pendulous sporangia. The compression genus *Metacalamostachys* is similar, but only one sporangium is borne on each sporangiophore.

In the Middle Carboniferous *Cingularia*, one species has whorled appendages, the upper portions of which are fused into a disclike structure with free tips, and the lower portions of which are flattened fertile structures, each with two pendant sporangia (Fig. 6-4C).

Macrostachya is an imperfectly known compression genus that is separated from others on the basis of its large size. If the structure were better known, it is likely that it would be grouped with *Calamostachys* or *Palaeostachya*.

An interesting cone genus resembling *Calamostachys* has been described by Dr. R. W. Baxter (personal communication) from the Kansas Carboniferous. Both megasporangiate and microsporangiate fructifications are known. The seed habit is closely approximated in the megasporangiate cone where each sporangium contains but one functional megaspore that is retained in the sporangium. At maturity, the entire sporangium was shed as a unit. This phenomenon, which so closely parallels the situation in *Lepidocarpon* of the Lycopsida, is previously unreported for the Sphenopsida.

EQUISETALES

As was seen among the Lycopsida, more nearly herbaceous forms of the Sphenopsida were contemporaneous with the arborescent giants during the Carboniferous period, and it is not unlikely that this herbaceous line, represented by the Equisetales, persisted long after the arborescent forms became extinct.

Phyllotheca is a genus known from the Upper Carboniferous, abundant in the Permian, and extending into the Lower Cretaceous. It was a branched form, with slender, tapered leaves borne in whorls at the nodes. Each leaf whorl was fused into a basal sheath. Peltate sporangiophores, very similar to those in *Equisetum*, were borne in clusters between adjacent leaf whorls.

Schizoneura, a branched form that existed from the Permian to the Jurassic, had two large, flat, many-veined leaflike structures at the nodes. These apparently split later into six to eight segments, each with one vein (Fig. 6-1B). These plants, which grew up to two meters in height and attained a diameter of 1 to 2 cm, bore long catkinlike strobili on some of the slender branches.

The Triassic *Neocalamites* resembled in many ways the earlier and probably ancestral calamitean plants so abundant in the Paleozoic. Leaves in a whorl were separate to the very base, unlike the situation in *Annularia.*

More nearly resembling the extant *Equisetum* was the Mesozoic and Cenozoic *Equisetites.* As in *Equisetum,* leaves were reduced and scalelike, and cones terminated some of the branches. These cones consisted of an axis with many peltate sporangiophores. Unfortunately, nothing is known of the internal structure of *Equisetites.* It would be interesting to know whether *Equisetites* had secondary wood, and whether *Equisetum* might then be considered a reduced sphenopsid with only primary xylem, or whether *Equisetites* was an extreme herb even in the Mesozoic and lacked secondary growth even as do some of the giant equisetums of today.

SPHENOPHYLLALES

An order that has little to do with the evolution of modern sphenopsids, but that pursued its own independent line of evolution, is the Sphenophyllales. Reconstructions of *Sphenophyllum* vary according to interpretations of various workers. Some show it as an erect, terrestrial, self-supporting plant; others believe it was a lax or creeping form dependent upon other plants for support; still others think it grew in an aquatic environment. As is typical in the Sphenopsida, leaves were borne in whorls, with a range of 6 to 18 leaves per whorl. Each leaf is narrow at the base and flares toward the more distal portion. It may be only slightly notched at the tip or there may be deep clefts. One vein enters the base of the leaf and divides dichotomously in the lamina. Adventitious roots were borne along the stem, and some of the branches terminated in elongated strobili.

Unlike members of the Calamitales and Equisetales, *Sphenophyllum* stems were protostelic. In older stages, the triangular (in cross section), exarch protostele had secondary xylem (Fig. 6-2C). Secondary tracheids are smaller opposite the angles of the primary xylem, and the rays are more conspicuous and closer together. In *S. plurifoliatum* the rays are unusual in that they consist of short, horizontally aligned cells that abut against vertically extending parenchyma cells at the corners of the tracheids. Pitting is generally multiseriate bordered. Older stems are limited externally by plates of periderm (Fig. 6-2C). Roots are similar to stems in general structure except that they are diarch.

Many sphenophyllalean cones are extremely complex structures and may be homosporous or heterosporous. The basic structure of *Bowmanites* involves whorls of fused sterile bracts just above which are whorls of sporangiophores (Fig. 6-4D). Because the sporangiophores may be fused to the upper surface of the bract whorl, it often seems as if the sporangiophores actually arise from the bracts. Each sporangiophore is branched; thus sometimes three or more axes may be present, each with generally a single recurved sporangium. The branches of the sporangiophores may be of varying lengths, so that the sporangia may become packed two or more deep between successive sterile whorls.

Litostrobus, a sphenopsid cone from the Middle Pennsylvanian, appears to have some affinity with the Sphenophyllales. It has alternating whorls of 12 fused bracts and 6 sporangiophores, each with one sporangium.

One of the most complex sphenopsid fructifications, often thought to be allied somehow to the Sphenophyllales, is the Lower Carboniferous genus *Cheirostrobus*. The fragment described was 4 cm in diameter and about 10 cm in length. In one whorl are 12 sporangiophores, each of which branched into two members, an upper and a lower, a short distance from the point of attachment. The upper branch was the fertile portion; the lower was completely sterile. The sterile appendage was further divided into three members, each of which extended outward horizontally and then bent upward abruptly. The fertile branch was also divided into three units, each above one of the sterile members below. Each of the three fertile segments bore at the distal end four extremely elongated, inwardly directed sporangia. Thus the fertile branches of each sporangiophore had 12 sporangia. With a total of 12 sporangiophores in a whorl, there would be 144 sporangia at one node! The number of sporangia in an entire cone must have been enormous, and the spore output considerable. All of the spores examined are of one type, suggesting that *Cheirostrobus* might have been homosporous.

In summarizing the Sphenopsida, it appears that the following trends occurred in the evolution of the group. Earliest forms retained much of the primitive dichotomous branching, while later types were more typically monopodial. Leaves of some of the earlier, more primitive sphenopsids were dichotomously branched, and later, more specialized types were unbranched. Modern sphenopsids have leaves that are much reduced and represented only by insignificant scales. Some of the Devonian sphenopsids were characterized by slender, dichotomously branched sporangiophores; more advanced forms have peltate sporangiophores, with sporangia directed toward the cone axis. There was also a conspicuous trend from loose, catkinlike strobili to compact cones.

An interesting and credible series of evolutionary steps in the development of sphenopsid sporangiophores is presented by the telome theory. From an original, three-dimensional branching fertile telome complex might have evolved a form with recurved terminal sporangia. The telomic segments could have become shortened, and eventually four or more recurved sporangia would have clustered together. Peltation would then be the final step, and sporangiophores such as those in *Pothocites* or in *Equisetum* would be the outcome.

The significance of the bract whorls in many extinct sphenopsid cones is not clearly understood. It is not known whether the sterile whorls simply represent branches of once-fertile members or whether they were always distinct units. The Upper Devonian-Lower Carboniferous *Pothocites* had cones with no sterile members included, while later types, such as *Palaeostachya* and *Calamostachys*, had alternating sterile and fertile whorls. *Equisetum*, however, has strobili consisting only of fertile whorls. Perhaps *Phyllotheca* may provide a key to the answer. Here sporangiophores are clustered on axes between adjacent sterile whorls. A more regular association of bracts and sporangiophores may have resulted in cones such as *Palaeostachya*, *Calamostachys*, and *Mazostachys*. Lack of any kind of association of fertile members with bracts is represented in cones of *Equisetites* and *Equisetum*. In *Bowmanites* there is an intimate relationship between subtending bract and sporangiophore.

REFERENCES

ABBOTT, MAXINE L., 1958. "The American species of *Asterophyllites, Annularia,* and *Sphenophyllum*," *Bull. Amer. Paleont.*, **38**: 289–390.

ANANIEV, A. R., 1957. "New plant fossils from the Lower Devonian of Torgachino in the southeastern part of West Siberia," *Botan. Zhur. S.S.S.R.*, **42**: 691–702.

ANDREWS, H. N., 1952. "Some American petrified calamitean stems," *Ann. Missouri Botan. Gard.*, **39**: 189–218.

———, and S. H. MAMAY, 1951. "A new American species of *Bowmanites*," *Botan. Gaz.*, 113: 158–165.

ARNOLD, C. A., 1958. "Petrified cones of the genus *Calamostachys* from the Carboniferous of Illinois," *Univ. Michigan Contrib. Mus. Paleont.*, **14**: 149–165.

BAXTER, R. W., 1948. "A study of the vegetative anatomy of the genus *Sphenophyllum*," *Ann. Missouri Botan. Gard.*, **35**: 209–231.

———, 1955. "*Palaeostachya Andrewsii*, a new species of calamitean cone from the American Carboniferous," *Amer. J. Botan.*, **42**: 342–351.

DELEVORYAS, T., 1955. "A *Palaeostachya* from the Pennsylvanian of Kansas," *Amer. J. Botan.*, **42**: 481–488.

EGGERT, D. A., 1962. "The ontogeny of Carboniferous arborescent Sphenopsida," *Palaeontographica* (in press).

HOSKINS, J. H., and A. T. CROSS, 1943. "Monograph of the Paleozoic cone genus *Bowmanites* (Sphenophyllales)," *Amer. Midl. Nat.*, **30**: 113–163.

KNOELL, HILDE, 1935. "Zur Kenntnis der strukturbietenden Pflanzenreste des jüngeren Palaeozoikum. 4 Zur Systematik der strukturbietenden Calamiten der Gattung *Arthropitys* Goeppert aus dem mittleren Oberkarbon Westdeutschlands und Englands," *Palaeontographica*, **80B**: 1–51.

KOSANKE, R. M., 1955. "*Mazostachys*—a new calamite fructification," *Illinois Geol. Surv. Rep. Invest.*, **180**: 1–37.

KRÄUSEL, R., and H. WEYLAND, 1926. "Beiträge zur Kenntnis der Devonflora. II," *Abhandl. senckenberg. naturforsch. Ges.*, **40**: 115–155.

———, 1929. "Beiträge zur Kenntnis der Devonflora. III," *Abhandl. senckenberg. naturforsch. Ges.*, **41**: 315–360.

———, 1932. "Pflanzenreste aus dem Devon. III. Über *Hyenia* Nath," *Senckenbergiana*, **14**: 274–280.

LECLERCQ, SUZANNE, 1940. "Contribution à l'étude de la flore du Dévonien de Belgique," *Acad. Roy. Belgique Mem.*, **12** (fasc. 3): 1–65.

———, and H. N. ANDREWS, JR., 1960. "*Calamophyton bicephalum*, a new species from the Middle Devonian of Belgium," *Ann. Missouri Botan. Gard.*, **47**: 1–23.

MÄGDEFRAU, K., 1956. *Paläobiologie der Pflanzen*, 3rd ed., Jena: Gustav Fischer.

Mamay, S. H., 1954. "A new sphenopsid cone from Iowa," *Ann. Botan.*, n.s., **18:** 229–239.

Scott, D. H., 1897. "On *Cheirostrobus*, a new type of fossil cone from the Lower Carboniferous strata (Calciferous Sandstone series)," *Phil. Trans. Roy. Soc. London,* **189:** 1–34.

Selling, O., 1944. "Studies on calamitean cone compressions by means of serial sections," *Svensk Botan. Tidskr.,* **38:** 295–330.

Steinman, G., and W. Elberskirch, 1929. "Neue bemerkenswerte Funde im ältesten Unterdevon des Wahnbachtales bei Siegburg," *Sitz. Nieder. Geol. Ver.,* **1927/28 C:** 1–74.

Walton, J., 1949. "On some Lower Carboniferous Equisetineae from the Clyde area. I. *Protocalamostachys arranensis* gen. et sp. nov. — a hitherto undescribed type of strobilus. II. The nodal structure of *Asterocalamites Göpperti* Solms sp.," *Trans. Roy. Soc. Edinburgh,* **61:** 729–736.

Weiss, C. E., 1876. "Beiträge zur fossilen Flora. Steinkohlen-Calamarien, mit besonderer Berücksichtigung ihrer Fructificationen," *Abhandl. geol. Specialkarte Pruss. Thüring. Staat,* **2** (1): 1–149.

chapter seven

Subdivision
Pteropsida
Class Pterophyta

Included in the subdivision Pteropsida are ferns and fernlike
plants and the seedbearing plants. Although there seems to be quite
a range of plant types included in this group, certain features suggest that there is a natural affinity among the members. Furthermore, a group of seed plants, the pteridosperms, seem to combine
features found in ferns with some found in typical gymnosperms.

Ferns and certain fossil fernlike plants comprise the class
Pterophyta, the members of which have true roots, stems, and leaves.
Leaves are thought to have evolved from systems of branches and,
in medullated stems, leaf gaps are usually (although not consistently)
present above the point of separation of a leaf trace. Sporangia in
the Pterophyta are terminal on leaf segments, marginal, or abaxial.
These sporangia may be borne on relatively unmodified foliage, or
there may be highly specialized fertile foliar organs. Sporangia may
be borne singly, in soral clusters, or they may be fused into synangia.
Although most ferns are homosporous, a large number, especially
among the fossil forms, are heterosporous.

Some of the earliest fernlike plants defy classification into any
of the established taxa. In fact, some can be only tentatively included in the Pterophyta, but are retained there because they have
certain fernlike characteristics.

Fig. 7-1. Reconstruction of the Devonian *Protopteridium hostimense*, the ultimate portions of which resemble fern leaves. At the lower right is a diagram of a sporangial cluster and one of a section through an axis with the stele stippled. (Redrawn from Kräusel and Weyland, 1933.)

The Middle Devonian *Protopteridium* (Fig. 7-1), for example, combines features of the Psilophytales with those of the Pterophyta. In fact, it is a genus of considerable significance in that it shows the possible evolution of at least certain ferns from psilophytic ancestors. Axes of *Protopteridium* are dichotomously or sympodially branched; distally they are pinnately branched. Near the tips fernlike laminae were produced by tissue formed between the pinnate segments. The tips may even be circinately coiled. Sporangia are found on some of the terminal branchlets.

Other genera of Paleozoic fernlike plants have been established from small petrified fragments. Although a definite affinity with ferns cannot be guaranteed, there seems to be no other group to which they may be assigned. Perhaps if more were known about them, one or more additional classes of vascular plants would be instituted.

Three of these genera, the Middle Devonian *Arachnoxylon, Reimannia,* and *Iridopteris,* are all characterized by variously lobed protosteles in the axes. In the tips of the "arms" of the steles are one or more small rods of parenchyma and possibly protoxylem. The presence of such peripheral pockets of protoxylem and parenchyma is noticeable among certain ferns of the order Coenopteridales, and it is largely for this reason that the Devonian petrified stem fragments are thought to represent fernlike plants.

The somewhat younger New Albany shale plants (Upper Devonian-Lower Mississippian) *Reimanniopsis* and *Stenokoleos* show a fairly similar stem structure.

A Middle and Upper Devonian fern, much larger than those just considered, is *Eospermatopteris.* Although the name suggests seed plant affinities, there is no doubt that it represents a true arborescent fern 20 or more feet in height, with a trunk as much as 3 feet in diameter near the base. Casts of stumps of *Eospermatopteris* are relatively abundant, and many are found in museums and in university geology or botany department collections. The long frondlike leaves were pinnately constructed, with the ultimate members modified into dichotomously forked pinnules. Small seedlike bodies 3 by 5.5 mm in size are actually sporangia packed full of spores.

It is thought by many paleobotanists that *Eospermatopteris* is identical to the European *Aneurophyton,* also Middle Devonian in age. The stem of *Aneurophyton* has a three-angled primary xylem strand with abundant secondary xylem consisting of tracheids and uniseriate rays. Sometimes *Protopteridium, Eospermatopteris,* and *Aneurophyton* are included in the order Protopteridiales.

CLADOXYLALES

Another order of fernlike plants from the Paleozoic, and one that is perhaps not completely natural, is the Cladoxylales, largely Devonian and Carboniferous. The Middle and Upper Devonian *Cladoxylon scoparium* (Fig. 7-2) is branched irregularly or dichotomously, and on the axes are small, apparently flattened, dichotomously branched leaves. Fertile axes bore fan-shaped, dichotomous appendages with free tips, each of which bore a sporangium. This species is thought to have been homosporous.

The Lower Carboniferous *C. mirabile* is known from petrifactions. The stem had a polystele and each individual stele had a long and sinuous outline in transverse section. Peripheral protoxylem occurred near the tips of the xylem arms. Secondary xylem was common around the primary strands. Leaf traces arise by a pinching off of tips of the xylem strands.

Another petrifaction genus, *Voelkelia,* which is Lower Carboniferous, has a dozen or more steles, with more secondary xylem produced toward the center of the stem than toward the outside (Fig. 7-9A). The steles are somewhat elongated radially and have no rays in the secondary xylem. Nothing other than the stem fragment is known, however.

COENOPTERIDALES

A very perplexing but highly interesting group of fernlike plants found in Paleozoic deposits are included in the order Coenopteridales. It is admittedly an artificial order, but it is retained for convenience until more is known about the members in it. An arbitrary subdivision of the order into four families might be considered. These are: Stauropteridaceae, Botryopteridaceae, Anachoropteridaceae, and Zygopteridaceae. In the Carboniferous *Stauropteris* (Fig. 7-4B) the stele is four-lobed, and the lobes may even be separate from each other. Branch traces originate

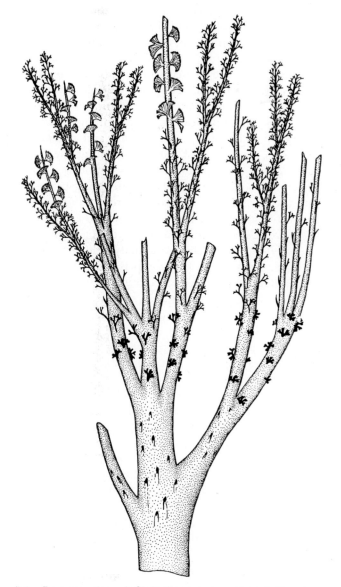

Fig. 7-2. Reconstruction of *Cladoxylon scoparium*. Note forking leaves and sporangia terminal on flattened dichotomizing axes. (Redrawn from Kräusel and Weyland, 1926.)

simultaneously from two adjacent lobes, and the steles of the resulting axes are also four-lobed. This branching pattern is repeated in successive axes. Externally, then, a reconstruction of *S. oldhamia* shows paired appendages, with two scalelike aphlebiae at each level of branching. Ultimate branches of *S. oldhamia* terminate in small spherical sporangia that have an outer conspicuous wall layer, and inner, more delicate ones. *Stauropteris burntislandica* is heterosporous, with elongated, pedicellate megasporangia (Fig. 7-9E). The megasporangium is about 1.3 mm long, and except for the very tip it is sterile. A small, flask-shaped portion at the distal end usually contains two megaspores. The heterosporous *S. burntislandica* is Lower Carboniferous, and, it is interesting to note, older than the Upper Carboniferous and homosporous *S. oldhamia*.

The Botryopteridaceae include the single genus *Botryopteris*, which ranged from the Lower Carboniferous to the Permian. *Botryopteris antiqua* (which may not actually belong to the genus) has protostelic stem axes that give rise to petioles with solid strands. A more typical *Botryopteris* has a protostelic stem, with petioles containing a trace having three arms in cross section (shaped like the Greek letter ω) (Fig. 7-4C). Traces to lateral members of the leaf systems are derived from one of the lateral arms of the petiole trace, and ultimate portions of the branching system had pinnae and pinnules (Fig. 7-3). Sporangia were generally borne in densely packed spherical masses, each with thousands of stalked sporangia. Sporangia at the periphery of the globose cluster were sterile and had a structure different from the annulate fertile ones within. Just how spores were dispersed from such a tightly packed cluster of sporangia is not known.

An unusual feature of some species of *Botryopteris* is the occurrence of stems on *petiole* axes; these stems, in turn, produced additional leaves. Perhaps the explanation lies in the fact that *Botryopteris* leaves had not yet become totally differentiated from stem systems and thus possessed characteristics of both stems and leaves. As will be seen below, other coenopterid ferns show the same feature.

The Carboniferous *Anachoropteris* is the type genus of the family Anachoropteridaceae. Petioles of *Anachoropteris* have traces that were flattened strands abaxially curved, unlike the more typical situation in modern ferns, which usually have adaxially

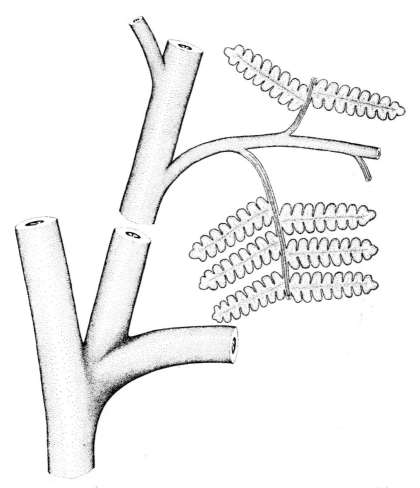

Fig. 7-3. Reconstruction of a portion of the frond system of a member of the genus *Botryopteris*. (From Delevoryas and Morgan, 1954a.)

curved petiole traces. *Anachoropteris involuta* petioles arising from protostelic stems have been described; these stems resemble closely those of *Tubicaulis,* discussed below. In one species, *A. clavata,* stem traces arose from one of the petiole trace arms and increased in diameter at higher levels (Fig. 7-5A, F). These stems gave rise to leaf traces, each resembling the parent petiole trace. *Chorionopteris* is a leaflike, pinnately lobed structure with marginal synangia, and

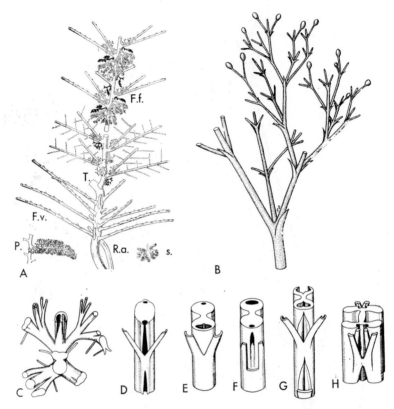

Fig. 7-4. A, diagrammatic reconstruction of a portion of *Rhacophyton zygopteroides*. T. — stem; F.v. — sterile pinnae; F.f. — fertile pinnae; R.a. — adventitious root; P. — pinna with pinnules; S. — sporangial cluster. (From Leclercq, 1951.) B, *Stauropteris oldhamia*, reconstruction. Note branches arising in pairs, scalelike aphlebiae, and terminal sporangia. (Modified from Zimmermann, 1949.) C, three-dimensional representation of the xylem of a portion of *Botryopteris trisecta* showing the cylindrical, central stem xylem from which originate, in three ranks, vascular systems to lateral appendages. (Redrawn from Mamay and Andrews, 1950.) D, portion of the vascular system of a phyllophore of *Dineuron pteroides* showing departure of paired pinna traces. E, xylem of part of the phyllophore of *Metaclepsydropsis duplex* with a pair of pinna traces. F, *Metaclepsydropsis duplex* with part of the pinna trace cut away to show "closing" of peripheral loop. G, portion of the xylem of the phyllophore of *Diplolabis Roemeri* with pinna traces arising in pairs. H, part of phyllophore trace of *Etapteris Scotti* (phyllophore of *Zygopteris*) showing pinna traces originating as separate strands, fusing above, and separating again at a still higher level. (D–H redrawn from Posthumus, 1925.)

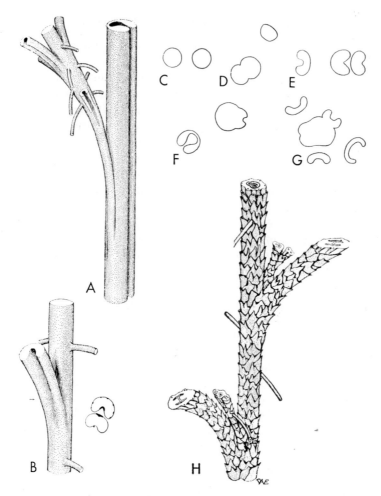

Fig. 7-5. A, xylem of petiole trace of *Anachoropteris clavata* from which the xylem of a stem stele branches off. The stem stele is a terete protostele from which arise adventitious roots and other petioles. (From Delevoryas and Morgan, 1954b.) B, diagrammatic representation of the xylem of the stem stele of *Apotropteris minuta* with an abaxially curved petiole trace. Small terete strands represent root traces. The cross section is one at a level represented by the arrow; black areas indicate protoxylem position. (From Morgan and Delevoryas, 1954.) C–G, diagrammatic cross sections of a series of stem steles and traces showing a possible origin of abaxially curved petiole traces in the Anachoropteridaceae. C, psilophytic plant. D, *Botryopteris antiqua*. E, *Apotropteris minuta*. F, *Anachoropteris clavata*. G, *Tubicaulis multiscalariformis*. (C–G from Morgan and Delevoryas, 1954.) H, reconstruction of a portion of a plant of *Ankyropteris glabra*. (From Eggert, 1959.)

is thought to represent the fructification of one of the anachorop-
terids.

Tubicaulis, from the Carboniferous and Permian periods, is
somewhat better known. It has a protostelic stem from which
originate many spirally arranged petioles, each with an abaxially
curved, C-shaped trace (Fig. 7-5G). The Lower Permian *Grammatopteris* is similar, but the traces to petioles are generally
uncurved and are simply tangentially expanded, flat bands of
tissue.

A small Upper Carboniferous coenopterid, *Apotropteris
minuta,* is a related form (Fig. 7-5B, E). Its protostelic stem has
small tracheids in the center, and a large segment of the stele is
involved in the formation of a leaf trace; traces have abaxial
curvature. *Psalixochlaena cylindrica* (formerly *Botryopteris cylindrica*) may be an identical form.

Petioles of the Zygopteridaceae (Devonian to Permian) are the
most complex of all of the coenopterids. They are most often
bilaterally symmetrical, and the plane of the pinna is perpendicular
to that of the main axis, unlike modern ferns, which generally have
pinnae flattened in the same plane as the frond axis. In the
Zygopteridaceae, furthermore, pinnae originating from the larger
ones are in a plane perpendicular to that of the parent pinnae, so
that a three-dimensional frond resulted. Because the petioles had
many stem characteristics, the noncommittal term "phyllophore"
is often applied to them. Most of the zygopterid phyllophore traces
have a characteristic patch of protoxylem and parenchyma near the
tip of each arm.

The Upper Devonian *Asteropteris* is among the older coenopterids, and in cross section the protostelic stem stele has about
a dozen radiating arms, each with a rod of parenchyma near the
tip. Petioles appear to have been borne in whorls, and traces to
them began as tangentially expanded strands with a rod of parenchyma near each edge. Higher up, two such rods are present near
the edge of each arm. Although *Asterochlaena* is a much younger
form, found in Lower Permian deposits, it exhibits many features
similar to those in *Asteropteris. Asterochlaena* has an elaborate
actinostele, with parenchyma and smaller xylem elements radiating
in each arm. Leaf traces are tangentially expanded and exhibit a
strand of parenchyma and protoxylem near each edge.

Although *Clepsydropsis* ranges from the Devonian to the Permian, the stem is known in only one species, *C. australis,* which has a five-armed actinostele with central mixed pith and tracheids. The petiole trace of *Clepsydropsis* is tangentially expanded, with a slight constriction in the middle. A strand of parenchyma and protoxylem is embedded in the tip of each arm. Pinna traces are formed by a pinching of the petiole trace near the edge; these pinna traces may produce traces to still smaller axes, in a plane perpendicular to that of the main frond.

The Lower Carboniferous *Metaclepsydropsis* has a simpler stem stele; it is a terete strand with central mixed tracheids and pith. Petiole traces resemble those of *Clepsydropsis,* but the middle constriction is more pronounced (Fig. 7-4E, F). Furthermore, the islands of parenchyma and protoxylem in the lateral parts of the arms are much larger than those in petiole traces of *Clepsydropsis.* Pinna traces arise in pairs from the edge of the petiole trace. The two pinna traces are fused together at their level of separation, but become distinct higher up and lie in a plane perpendicular to that of the petiole trace. Just below the region of separation of the pinnae from the petiole are two flaps of tissue called aphlebiae. These minute vascularized structures are common among many of the zygopterids.

The stem of the Carboniferous and Permian *Zygopteris* is protostelic, with the central portion consisting of tracheids and parenchyma. Surrounding this zone is a mass of radiating xylem cells. Some workers believe that these cells represent secondary xylem, while others consider them to be simply radially aligned primary cells. Petiole traces are H-shaped in transverse section, and because of their resemblance to the Greek letter *eta,* isolated petioles were called *Etapteris* before they were found attached to stems (Fig. 7-4H). Although there are no distinct peripheral loops, on each of the broad faces of the petiole trace is a depression in which protoxylem is placed, that would correspond to an opened peripheral loop. Pinna traces begin separately, in pairs, at each edge of the depressed furrow, are fused at a higher level, and still higher are freed again. Sporangia of *Zygopteris* are known; they are borne in clusters, are elongated, and have two opposite longitudinal annuli. *Biscalitheca* is very similar, but the plant that bore it is unknown. Another similar genus, also found isolated, is *Monoscalitheca,* with a single annulus. As far as is known, all of these forms are homosporous.

Ankyropteris, known from the Pennsylvanian and Permian, is represented by stem and phyllophore fragments (Fig. 7-5H). A generally five-sided xylem strand traversed the stem and was composed of a central region having a mixture of small tracheids and parenchyma cells and an outer region with larger elements. Phyllophore traces are roughly H-shaped and are oriented with two of the arms directed toward the stem. A broad, flat band of parenchyma and small tracheids is situated in each flank of the H-shaped trace. A feature of considerable interest in *Ankyropteris,* and one uncommon among fernlike plants, is the occurrence of axillary branching. In some specimens the phyllophore trace and axillary branch trace depart from the stele as a common trace and become separated at a higher level. Other specimens have axillary branch steles that separate directly from the stem stele at a level above that of the separation of the phyllophore trace. The axillary branch is a duplicate of the main axis, although it is somewhat smaller. It, too, gives off phyllophores and bears branches. Thus it is possible to consider a wide range of sizes of *Ankyropteris* specimens as representing different orders of branching. It appears that the ultimate portions of the phyllophore systems terminated in foliar laminae. Covering the stem and phyllophores is a dense mass of scalelike aphlebiae that were probably also photosynthetic.

From the foregoing account of the Coenopteridales it can readily be seen that they represent a fascinating but puzzling group of plants. It is obvious that certain differences exist among the many members, suggesting that more than one order of plants is involved. Homospory and heterospory occur in this group. Some sporangia are massively eusporangiate; others approach a leptosporangiate condition. Some forms had well-developed fern fronds; others possibly lacked expanded laminar portions. Branching ranges from dichotomous to axillary.

In spite of the pronounced heterogeneity in the order, there are certain evolutionary patterns evident. Among the Zygopteridaceae, for example, a petiole trace like that of *Clepsydropsis* might be considered to represent a primitive type. The stem of *Dineuron* (Lower Carboniferous) is unknown, but the petiole also has two peripheral loops with no constriction in the middle. Pinnae are given off in pairs on either side of the petiole (Fig. 7-4D). An expansion of the peripheral loops and a more pronounced constriction leads to a type like *Metaclepsydropsis*. The Lower Carboniferous *Diplolabis* (Fig. 7-4G) represents an even more advanced elaboration of this trend. If the two lateral portions of the phyllophore trace of *Metaclepsydropsis* were expanded radially, an H-shaped *Ankyropteris*-type trace would result, with broad, flat peripheral loops. *Zygopteris* petioles might have resulted from an opening of the lateral peripheral loops and a radial expansion of the trace arms without a corresponding increase in size of the now-open peripheral loop. The evolutionary trends that have been suggested need not be interpreted as indicating natural affinities among the members, but rather, as illustrating manifestations of various degrees of evolutionary advance along lines of petiole trace differentiation.

An evolutionary story might also be read among the Anachoropteridaceae with the typical abaxially curved petiole traces (Fig. 7-5C-G). Such forms could have had a psilophytic origin where dichotomous branching produced pairs of axes with equal dimensions. In *Botryopteris antiqua* one member of the branching is somewhat smaller than the other and represents the beginning of a leaf system. *Apotropteris minuta* shows a slight abaxial curvature of the trace, yet a considerable part of the stem stele is involved in trace formation; no regular phyllotaxy is evident. *Anachoropteris* and *Tubicaulis* have more closely arranged nodes, more pronounced abaxial curvature, and helical leaf arrangement. Only a small part of the stele is involved in trace formation.

Probably the closest known ancestral types of the coenopterids were the Psilophytales. Indeed, many of the coenopterids show little distinction between stem and leaf, and protostelic axes are rather common. Among the various members of the Coenopteridales, there had been varying specialization of some of the vegetative parts, resulting in some of the elegant but complex vascular patterns in stems and petioles. Many workers see in the Coenopteridales a possible source for the later, more typical ferns. This is an attractive idea, but it involves many difficulties that cannot be overcome. Ferns, some of them closely related to modern taxa, were contemporaneous with many of the coenopterids, from which they were supposed to have been derived. Some of these ferns were giant arborescent forms. Another difficulty involves the vascular pitting.

Most of the coenopterids had multiseriate pitting, often with closely spaced bordered pits. This type of pitting is more highly specialized than that in the largest number of ferns. Furthermore, the Coenopteridales seem to represent a high degree of specialization in themselves and do not appear to represent a group "plastic" enough to have been of much significance in the subsequent evolution of ferns.

Whether or not the Coenopteridales were important in evolutionary developments within the ferns, it cannot be denied that they were an important element in the forests of the Paleozoic and must have formed much of the ground cover as well as having been epiphytic on some of the larger contemporary plants. These fernlike plants are conspicuously absent in reconstructions of Carboniferous forests and their inclusion in future attemps to portray these ancient forests would contribute considerably toward showing the real situation.

As was mentioned above, some modern fern families had close relatives existing in the Carboniferous. Certain of the tall, treelike ferns were members of the Marattiales, and foliage of ferns thought to belong to the same group is extremely abundant as compression fossils.

MARATTIALES

Petrified trunks of the Marattiales that existed in the Carboniferous and Permian belong to the genus *Psaronius* (Fig. 7-9B). These stems had an extremely complex structure, but resemble in many ways those of modern tree ferns (Fig. 7-6). Near the base of a plant the stem was narrow and was surrounded by a thick, dense mass of adventitious roots. Higher levels are broader, with a corresponding decrease in the diameter of the root mantle. Thus the stem was obconical, and much of the support was contributed by adventitious roots. The small, basal part of the stem had one, or perhaps two, amphiphloic siphonostelic stelar cycles. Leaves were helically arranged in a small number of orthostichies (Fig. 7-8A). Higher, as the stem increased in diameter, more stelar cycles were added, and more orthostichies were present (Fig. 7-8B). New stelar cycles were added internally at successively higher levels from the existing innermost cycles (Fig. 7-7). Quite high in the plant as

Fig. 7-6. Reconstruction of a plant of the genus *Psaronius* and its associated parts approximately 20 to 25 feet high. (From Morgan, 1959.)

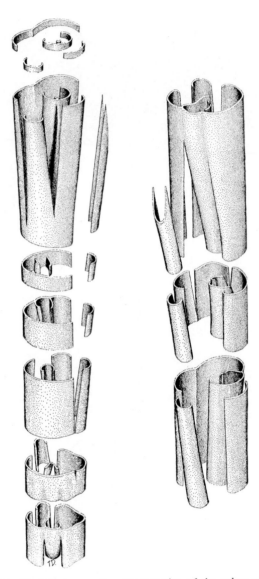

Fig. 7-7. Idealized diagrammatic representation of the xylem of a *Psaronius* stele near the basal part of the stem. The portion of the drawing at the right should be superposed above that portion on the left. (From Morgan, 1959.)

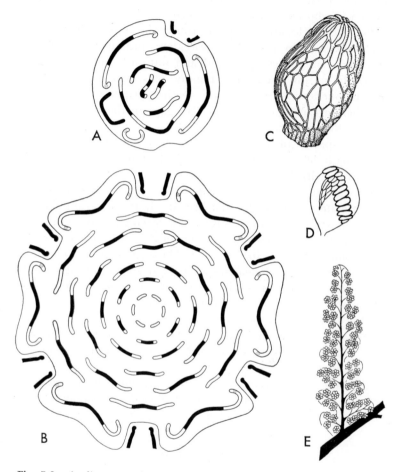

Fig. 7-8. A, diagrammatic transverse section of *Psaronius Blicklei* at a level with five orthostichies, helical leaf arrangement (2/5 phyllotaxy), and four stelar cycles. Leaf traces or potential leaf traces are in solid black. (Redrawn from Morgan, 1959.) B, transverse section of a distal portion of a stem of *Psaronius Blicklei* showing whorled leaf arrangement and twelve orthostichies. Solid black portions of bundles represent leaf traces or potential leaf traces. (Redrawn from Morgan, 1959.) C, sporangium of *Senftenbergia pennaeformis.* (Redrawn from Radforth, 1939.) D, sporangium of *Oligocarpia mixta.* (Redrawn from Abbott, 1954.) E, fertile pinna of *O. Brongniarti.* (Redrawn from Abbott, 1954.)

many as 12 cycles may have been present, and phyllotaxy in these regions was whorled, with up to as many as 14 orthostichies.

Psaronius steles are a system of concentric amphiphloic cauline strands separated by gaps. Leaf traces are initiated in the center of the stem and progress upward and outward, joining the free edges of the gaps in one cycle of the cauline system as they separate from an inner cycle on their way to the periphery of the stem. Thus there are regular "pathways" of gaps in the cauline system through which the traces pass (Fig. 7-8B).

Some species of *Psaronius* were distichous throughout the entire length of stem. Others never had more than four or six orthostichies with leaves in whorls.

Leaves attached to these stems were large, compound forms, with ultimate pinnules attached broadly at the base and having more or less parallel edges (Fig. 7-9F). Synangiate fructifications are found on the abaxial sides of some of these leaves and they resemble some of the sori in the extant Marattiales. In *Ptychocarpus* there are five to eight elongated sporangia arranged in a tight circle with a central core of sterile tissue. *Asterotheca* generally has fewer, more flattened sporangia in the circle, united only at the base. *Scolecopteris* is a genus with generally four to five shortly pedicellate, pointed sporangia (Fig. 7-9C). *Acitheca* is similar, but sessile, and with a short rod of sterile tissue uniting the sporangia at the base.

Mesozoic marattiaceous fossils are represented by leaves with sporangia. *Marattiopsis* is one and *Danaeopsis,* similar to the extant *Archangiopteris,* is another.

SCHIZAEACEAE

Another ancient family of ferns is the Schizaeaceae, which have relatives in the Carboniferous. A terminal annulus and longitudinal dehiscence of the sporangium are characteristic of the family. Sporangia with these characters are found in the Carboniferous *Senftenbergia* (Fig. 7-8C). *Klukia* is a Triassic and Jurassic genus with similar features. *Norimbergia,* with 9 to 12 abaxial sporangia per pinnule, is known from the Jurassic. *Schizaeopsis* is a Lower Cretaceous genus very close to the extant *Schizaea.* The Cretaceous *Ruffordia* resembles the modern *Anemia,* which itself occurs in the Mesozoic era (Fig. 7-10C). Fossil members of the genus *Lygodium*

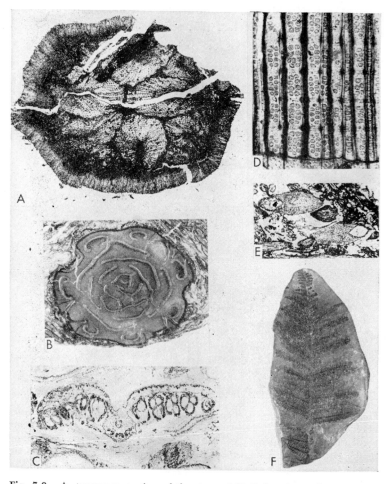

Fig. 7-9. A, transverse section of the stem of *Voelkelia refracta*. (From Delevoryas, 1955.) B, cross section of a stem of *Psaronius melanedrus* at a level with seven orthostichies and helical leaf arrangement. C, cross section of a pinna of *Scolecopteris minor* var. *parvifolia* with two attached pinnules and abaxial synangia. (From Morgan and Delevoryas, 1952.) D, radial section of the secondary xylem of *Callixylon Newberryi*. E, longitudinal sections of two megasporangia of *Stauropteris burntislandica*. Note the distal fertile region and the bulky, parenchymatous sterile portion. F, compression fossil showing *Pecopteris*-type foliage.

are known from Tertiary deposits. Thus it is evident that the Schizaeaceae represent an old family with an interesting and fairly continuous record since the Carboniferous period. Admittedly, assumed relationships of some of the members are based on sporangia alone, but the fact that schizaeaceous sporangia are so characteristic justifies these suggested affinities.

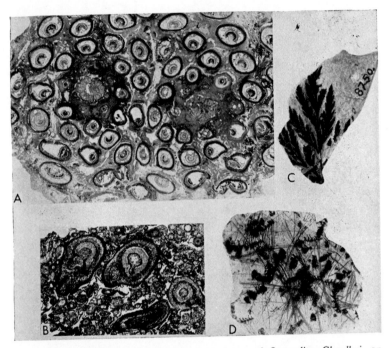

Fig. 7-10. A, transverse section of a specimen of *Osmundites Chandleri*, an Eocene fern, at a level just above a stem dichotomy. B, cross section of a small portion of the false stem of *Tempskya* cf. *minor*. C, small fragment of a leaf of *Anemia Fremonti*. D, compressed specimens of the Tertiary *Azolla primaeva*, an aquatic fern.

GLEICHENIACEAE

One feature of the family Gleicheniaceae is the occurrence of sporangia with oblique annuli and longitudinal dehiscence. The Carboniferous *Oligocarpia* has similar sporangia arranged on the abaxial surface of pinnules in little circular clusters (Fig. 7-8D, E). Some workers consider *Oligocarpia* to have close affinities with the Gleicheniaceae. *Gleichenites*, which extends from the Triassic to the Tertiary, has leaves much closer to the typical frond of the

Gleicheniaceae than the foliage on which *Oligocarpia* was borne. The fact that gleichenialike fossils are found back in the early Mesozoic strongly suggests that the family had Paleozoic origins.

OSMUNDACEAE

The Osmundaceae, with three living genera, had a much greater distribution in past geologic ages than in the present. Osmundaceous forms are known as far back as the Permian, with a subsequent fairly continuous fossil record. Anatomical characters of some of the fossil forms in this family suggest the sequence of events involved in the formation of leaf gaps and pith. A striking petrified genus with supposedly osmundaceous affinities is the late Permian *Thamnopteris* (Fig. 7-11A). It has a large protostele, with a central zone of tracheids wider and shorter than those in the outer zone. Leaf traces arose from the outer part of the stele and were solid strands at lower levels, and C-shaped, with adaxially directed arms, at higher levels. Tightly packed leaf bases at the periphery of the stem were rhombic in cross section. Although the innermost xylem elements in the stele of the Upper Permian *Zalesskya* are not preserved, this genus is thought to have a structure similar to that of *Thamnopteris*.

The Upper Triassic *Itopsidema* (Fig. 7-11B) is of interest because of the presence of a pith, with a very few scattered tracheids in it. The leaf traces arose from the outer part of the stele and assumed a C-shape in the cortex. A significant feature of this genus is that even though the stem is essentially siphonostelic, no gaps are present.

Osmundites extends from the Jurassic to the Tertiary. *Osmundites Kolbei,* from the Jurassic, and others, are siphonostelic, with leaf traces that left no gap at the level of their separation. There was a gap, however, at a slightly higher level, except in *O. Dunlopi* in which the parenchyma above the leaf trace does not quite dissect the stele. Some of the later Mesozoic members and the Tertiary species had leaf gaps more nearly similar to those in modern osmundas (Fig. 7-10A).

From the above brief description of petrified osmundaceous stems it becomes apparent that the pith in this family is intrastelar in origin, having evolved by a modification of innermost xylem elements in a protostele. The occurrence of Permian protostelic

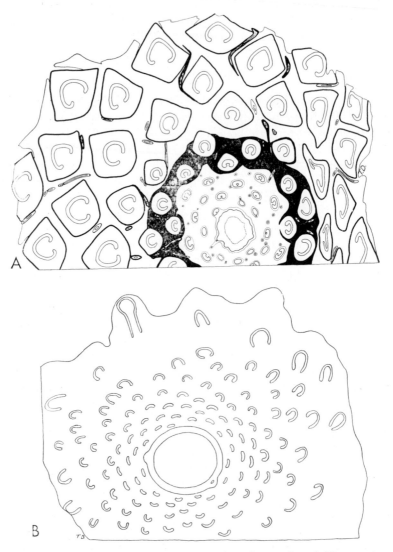

Fig. 7-11. A, diagrammatic transverse section of a portion of *Thamnopteris Schlechtendalii*, a Permian osmundaceous fern. (Drawing based on photograph in Kidston and Gwynne-Vaughan, 1909.) B, diagrammatic cross section of *Itopsidema Van Cleavei*, a Triassic fern from Arizona. (Drawing based on photograph in Daugherty, 1960.)

forms with a somewhat specialized inner portion and the discovery of a Triassic genus with only a few scattered tracheids in the parenchymatous pith strongly suggest the evolutionary sequence of development of the siphonostelic condition in the Osmundaceae. Furthermore, *Itopsidema*, although siphonostelic, has no leaf gaps, thus precluding the possibility of an "invasion" of extrastelar tissues into the center of the stele to produce a pith. It is quite possible, however, that other families of ferns may have undergone a different pattern of stelar evolution.

Leaf remains, thought to have been allied to the Osmundaceae, are abundant in the Mesozoic. *Todites* has leaves and sporangia like those in the Osmundaceae. *Cladophlebis,* another Mesozoic genus, is based primarily on sterile leaf material that has some resemblance to osmundaceous leaves.

MATONIACEAE

The Matoniaceae, currently with only two genera, was also once more widespread in the past. The leaf of *Matonia* is palmately divided, and sporangia have oblique annuli and are borne in a tight circle, not unlike those in the supposedly gleicheniaceous *Oligocarpia*. *Phlebopteris,* Triassic to Lower Cretaceous, has a simpler leaf construction, and when fertile foliage is found it can be seen that sporangia are like those in the modern *Matonia*. *Matonidium* is a closely related Jurassic and Cretaceous genus.

OTHER FERNS

Petrified trunks in the Mesozoic and Cenozoic suggest that the family Cyatheaceae has had a long history.

Azolla, the aquatic fern of the order Hydropteridales, occasionally has been found as compressions (Fig. 7-10D). At times structural details are surprisingly sharp, and maceration clearly reveals spore structure with associated reproductive peculiarities. Leaves of *Salvinia*, widespread in the Tertiary, are also known as compressions.

During the Cretaceous period there existed an unusual fern, *Tempskya,* that cannot be related with certainty to any of the modern families of ferns (Fig. 7-10B). *Tempskya* apparently was an arborescent plant, but the main axis was not just a single stem but many slender, branched stems held together within a compact mass of adventitious roots. The true stems had amphiphloic siphonosteles with conspicuous gaps formed by the separating leaf traces. A leaf trace became free at one edge at a level lower than that of the separation of the other edge of the C-shaped strand. Many specimens of *Tempskya* consist almost completely of roots, a situation that leads some workers to believe that conceivably the stems disintegrated below as they grew upward, so that the main bulk of the basal portions of the false trunks was composed of roots.

PROBLEMATICAL AND TRANSITIONAL FERNS

There existed during past geologic ages a number of fernlike plants difficult to categorize into any of the known taxa or that had structural features that might be considered transitional between the ferns and other groups. Although their taxonomic position is problematical, they are of considerable interest to the morphologist because they demonstrate the existence of plants that might be important in piecing together the story of early vascular plant evolution.

The Upper Devonian *Tetraxylopteris* appears to combine features of the true ferns, the Cladoxylales, and the pteridosperms (Fig. 7-12C). From the stem arose spirally arranged lateral appendages that, in turn, branched in a decussate manner. These lateral, three-dimensionally branched structures are thought to be homologous with leaves. At the tips of some of the leaflike appendages were large sporangia. The primary xylem in all the axes except the most distal ones was cruciform in section, and abundant secondary xylem was present. Secondary xylem was formed first in the depressions between adjacent primary xylem projections. It has been suggested that *Tetraxylopteris* and *Aneurophyton* be placed together in the order Aneurophytales.

Perhaps one of the most exciting finds in recent times is the discovery of fossils showing the identity, at least in part, of two genera, one assigned to the ferns (*Archaeopteris*), and the other formerly to the gymnosperms (*Callixylon*). *Archaeopteris* was common in late Devonian times (Fig. 7-12A); its fronds were large, up

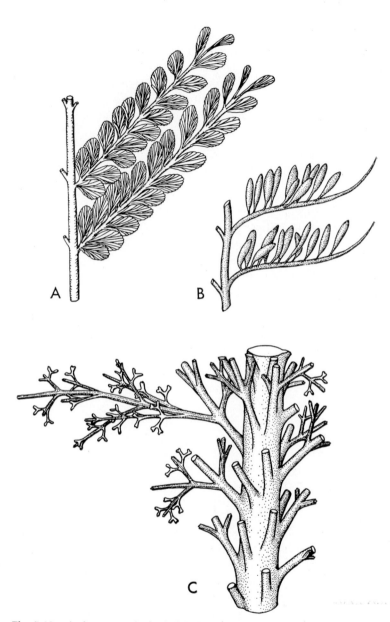

Fig. 7-12. A, fragment of a leaf of *Archaeopteris latifolia*. B, portion of a fertile region of the frond of *Archaeopteris latifolia*. (A and B, redrawn from Andrews, 1948, by permission of Univ. of Chicago Press.) C, reconstruction of a portion of *Tetraxylopteris Schmidtii*. (Redrawn from Beck, 1957.)

to a meter in length, with a straight rachis and subopposite pinnae. Pinnules were generally wedge-shaped, 1 to 5 cm long, and were borne in two rows on the pinnae. Venation in the pinnules was dichotomous, with a single trace entering the base of each pinnule. Certain of the pinnae were specialized into fertile branches on which elongated sporangia were produced in place of pinnules. One species, *A. latifolia*, was heterosporous (Fig. 7-12B).

Callixylon is the name assigned to stem fragments with pith, mesarch bundles slightly embedded in the pith, and abundant secondary xylem. Characteristic of the xylem are circular bordered pits borne in clusters on the radial walls and separated by areas of the pitless tracheid walls (Fig. 7-9D).

It had long been assumed that *Callixylon* was the wood of a gymnospermous plant in the order Cordaitales. Now it has been shown, however, that stems with a *Callixylon*-like structure bore fronds of *Archaeopteris,* and that the plant must have been a giant fern, with considerable lateral development. *Archaeopteris* is the older name, and now applies to the entire plant. (The name *Callixylon* is retained for some species of wood fragments that are not quite like those found belonging to *Archaeopteris*.) Although *Archaeopteris* is an undisputed cryptogam, it shows certain structural features that are transitional toward higher plants such as the seed ferns.

The Upper Devonian *Rhacophyton zygopteroides* is the best known species of the genus, and although it is primitive in many respects, it shows features similar to those of certain of the Zygopteridaceae (Fig. 7-4A). From an elongated stem arose lateral appendages, some of which represented sterile fronds, while others were fertile members. Each sterile frond rachis had two rows of pinnae, and on these pinna axes were dichotomously branched pinnulelike members. Pinnae on the fertile fronds were also two-ranked; each pinna was bifurcated a short distance from the point of its attachment, thus producing a three-dimensional frond system. Smaller pinnae were borne in two rows on the major pinnae, and dichotomously constructed pinnules, such as those on the sterile frond, were attached to the slender secondary pinnae. Sporangia terminate small axes of a dichotomizing system of branches that were attached on the underside of some of the forked pinnae, near the points of pinna attachment.

The paleobotanical history of the ferns has been responsible for the development of new ways of looking at the phylogeny of this ancient and widespread group. It is quite probable that dichotomously branched, psilophytelike plants may have been ancestral to ferns. The telome hypothesis as put forth by Zimmermann includes a series of steps that could have been manifested in the ferns and fernlike plants. Zimmermann would begin with a three-dimensional dichotomous system that had fertile terminal members. A subsequent planation of this branching structure, with more pronounced growth of some members over others, would lead to a sporangial system not too unlike that of *Protopteridium* or *Archaeopteris*. With development of sterile, photosynthetic tissue between the individual axes, a structure more closely resembling a leaf, with marginal sporangia, would result. Indeed, such fertile fernlike leaves are known in the fossil record; *Acrangiophyllum pendulatum* from the Pennsylvanian of Alabama has divided pinnules, with sporangia at the tips of the lobes. By the addition of more sterile tissue beyond the point of attachment of sporangia, pinnules with abaxial sporangia would be produced. The Carboniferous *Renaultia* has abaxial sporangia borne at the very edge of the frond, and most modern ferns have the more typical laminar sporangia, with sori in from the margin. Such a phyletic change from marginal sporangia to abaxial positions has been termed a "phyletic slide," although strictly speaking there has been no shift in position of sporangia, but, more probably, a more pronounced development of sterile tissue.

The presence in the Paleozoic of huge treelike ferns such as *Archaeopteris* and *Aneurophyton* with abundant secondary wood adds to the difficulty of interpreting the primitive condition of the ferns. In addition, not a few Devonian fernlike plants were heterosporous. Did modern, small herbaceous ferns come from large types with secondary xylem? Is the homosporous condition of most present-day ferns persistently primitive or are these types somehow descended from earlier heterosporous types? Some of these questions still cannot be answered. It is not unlikely that more than one group of early fernlike plants was ancestral to modern fern types. It is obvious that the fern frond has been derived independently among various groups of plants. Even gymnospermous plants, the seed ferns, have frondlike leaves closely resembling the leaves of true ferns. It is also possible that some fern groups may have originated as a result of loss of massive secondary vascular tissue, while others may have evolved along lines in which there never had been cambial activity.

The fact that ferns may represent a somewhat polyphyletic group may lead one to wonder just what a fern is and what characters hold the group Pterophyta together. In a broad sense, a fern might be defined as a megaphyllous vascular cryptogam with foliar sporangia. Of course, some of the earliest fernlike plants had not yet evolved structures that could definitely be called leaves, but as it has been noted before, transition types are to be expected, and precise classification is not always possible.

REFERENCES

ABBOTT, MAXINE L., 1954. "Revision of the Paleozoic fern genus *Oligocarpia*," *Palaeontographica*, **96B:** 39–65.

———, 1961. "A coenopterid fern fructification from the Upper Freeport No. 7 Coal in southeastern Ohio," *J. Paleont.*, **35:** 981–985.

ANDREWS, H. N., JR., 1948. "Some evolutionary trends in the pteridosperms," *Botan. Gaz.*, **110:** 13–31.

———, and ELLEN M. KERN, 1947. "The Idaho tempksyas and associated fossil plants," *Ann. Missouri Botan. Gard.*, **34:** 119–186.

ARNOLD, C. A., 1940. "Structure and relationships of some Middle Devonian plants from western New York," *Amer. J. Botan.* **27:** 57–63.

———, 1952. "Fossil Osmundaceae from the Eocene of Oregon," *Palaeontographica*, **92B:** 63–78.

———, 1955. "A Tertiary *Azolla* from British Columbia," *Univ. Michigan Contrib. Mus. Paleont.*, **12:** 37–45.

BAXTER, R. W., 1951. "*Ankyropteris glabra*, a new American species of the Zygopteridaceae," *Amer. J. Botan.*, **38:** 440–452.

———, 1952. "The coal-age flora of Kansas. II. On the relationships among the genera *Etapteris*, *Scleropteris* and *Botrychioxylon*," *Amer. J. Botan.*, **39:** 263–274.

BECK, C. B., 1957. "*Tetraxylopteris schmidtii* gen. et sp. nov., a probable pteridosperm precursor from the Devonian of New York," *Amer. J. Botan.*, **44:** 350–367.

———, 1960. "Studies of New Albany shale plants. I. *Stenokoleos simplex* comb. nov.," *Amer. J. Botan.*, **47:** 115–124.

———, 1960. "The identity of *Archaeopteris* and *Callixylon*," *Brittonia*, **12:** 351–368.

BERTRAND, P., 1911. "Structure des stipes d'*Asterochlaena laxa* Stenzel," *Mem. Soc. Geol. Nord.*, **7** (1): 1–72.

DAUGHERTY, L., 1960. "*Itopsidema*, a new genus of the Osmundaceae from the Triassic of Arizona," *Amer. J. Botan.*, **47**: 771–777.

DELEVORYAS, T., and JEANNE MORGAN, 1951. "*Tubicaulis multiscalariformis*: a new American coenopterid," *Amer. J. Botan.*, **39**: 160–166.

——, 1954a. "Observations on petiolar branching and foliage of an American *Botryopteris*," *Amer. Midl. Nat.*, **52**: 374–387.

——, 1954b. "A further investigation of the morphology of *Anachoropteris clavata*," *Amer. J. Botan.*, **41**: 192–198.

EGGERT, D. A., 1959. "Studies of Paleozoic ferns. The morphology, anatomy and taxonomy of *Ankyropteris glabra*," *Amer. J. Botan.*, **46**: 510–520.

——, 1959. "Studies of Paleozoic ferns: *Tubicaulis stewartii* sp. nov. and evolutionary trends in the genus," *Amer. J. Botan.*, **46**: 594–602.

GOLDRING, WINIFRED, 1924. "The Upper Devonian forest of seed ferns in eastern New York," *New York State Mus. Bull.*, **251**: 50–72.

GORDON, W. T., 1911. "On the structure and affinities of *Metaclepsydropsis duplex* (Williamson)," *Trans. Roy. Soc. Edinburgh*, **48**: 163–190.

HALL, J. W., 1961. "*Anachoropteris involuta* and its attachment to a *Tubicaulis* type of stem from the Pennsylvanian of Iowa," *Amer. J. Botan.*, **48**: 731–737.

HIRMER, M., 1927. *Handbuch der Paläobotanik*, Munich and Berlin: R. Oldenbourg.

HOLDEN, H. S., 1960. "The morphology and relationships of *Rachiopteris cylindrica*," *Bull. Brit. Mus. (Nat. Hist.) Geol.*, **4**: 53–69.

KIDSTON, R., and D. T. GWYNNE-VAUGHAN, 1907. "On the fossil Osmundaceae. Part I," *Trans. Roy. Soc. Edinburgh*, **45**: 759–780.

——, 1958. "On the fossil Osmundaceae. Part II," *Trans. Roy. Soc. Edinburgh*, **46**: 213–232.

——, 1909. "On the fossil Osmundaceae. Part III," *Trans. Roy. Soc. Edinburgh*, **46**: 651–667.

——, 1910. "On the fossil Osmundaceae. Part IV," *Trans. Roy. Soc. Edinburgh*, **47**: 455–477.

——, 1914. "On the fossil Osmundaceae. Part V," *Trans. Roy. Soc. Edinburgh*, **50**: 469–480.

KRÄUSEL, R., and H. WEYLAND, 1926. "Beiträge zur Kenntnis der Devonflora. II," *Abhandl. senckenberg. naturforsch. Ges.*, **40**: 113–155.

——, 1933. "Die Flora des bömischen Mitteldevons," *Palaeontographica*, **78B**: 1–46.

KUBART, B., 1916. "Ein Beitrag zur Kenntnis von *Anachoropteris pulchra*, Corda," *Denkschr. K. Akad. Wiss. Wien (Math.-Nat. Kl.)*, **93**: 551–584.

LECLERCQ, SUZANNE, 1951. "Étude morphologique et anatomique d'une fougère du Dévonien supérieur," *Ann. Soc. Géol. Belgique*, **9**: 1–62.

MAMAY, S. H., 1950. "Some American Carboniferous fern fructifications," *Ann. Missouri Botan. Gard.*, **37**: 409–476.

——, 1955. "*Acrangiophyllum*, a new genus of Pennsylvanian Pteropsida based on fertile foliage," *Amer. J. Botan.*, **42**: 177–183.

——, 1957. "*Biscalitheca*, a new genus of Pennsylvanian coenopterids, based on its fructification," *Amer. J. Botan.*, **44**: 229–239.

——, and H. N. ANDREWS, 1950. "A contribution to our knowledge of the anatomy of *Botryopteris*," *Bull. Torrey Botan. Club*, **77**: 462–494.

Morgan, Jeanne, 1959. "The morphology and anatomy of American species of the genus *Psaronius*," *Illinois Biol. Monogr.*, **27.** Urbana, Ill.: Univ. Illinois Press.

———, and T. Delevoryas, 1952. "An anatomical study of *Stipitopteris*," *Amer. J. Botan.*, **39:** 474–478.

———, 1954. "An anatomical study of a new coenopterid and its bearing on the morphology of certain ccenopterid petioles," *Amer. J. Botan.*, **41:** 198–203.

Posthumus, O., 1924. "On some principles of stelar morphology," *Rec. Trav. Botan. Neérland*, **21:** 111–296.

Radforth, N., 1939. "Further contributions to our knowledge of the fossil Schizaeaceae: genus *Senftenbergia*," *Trans. Roy. Soc. Edinburgh*, **59:** 745–761.

Read, C. B., and R. W. Brown, 1937. "American Cretaceous ferns of the genus *Tempskya*," *U.S. Geol. Surv. Prof. Paper*, **186-F:** 105–131.

Sahni, B., 1928. "On *Clepsydropsis australis*, a zygopterid tree-fern with a *Tempskya*-like false stem, from the Carboniferous rocks of Australia," *Phil. Trans. Roy. Soc. London*, **217B:** 1–37.

———, 1932. "On the genera *Clepsydropsis* and *Cladoxylon* Unger, and on a new genus *Austroclepsis*," *New Phytol.*, **31:** 270–278.

———, 1932. "On a Palaeozoic tree-fern, *Grammatopteris Baldaufi* (Beck) Hirmer, a link between the Zygopterideae and the Osmundaceae," *Ann. Botan.*, **46:** 863–877.

———, 1932. "On the structure of *Zygopteris primaria* (Cotta) and on the relationship between the genera *Zygopteris*, *Etapteris* and *Botrychioxylon*," *Phil. Trans. Roy. Soc. London*, **222B:** 29–46.

Surange, K. R., 1952. "The morphology of *Stauropteris burntislandica* P. Bertrand and its megasporangium *Bensonites fusiformis* R. Scott," *Phil. Trans. Roy. Soc. London*, **237B:** 73–91.

Zimmermann, W., 1949. *Geschichte der Pflanzen*, Stuttgart: Georg Thieme Verlag.

———, 1952. "Main results of the 'telome theory'," *Palaeobotanist*, **1:** 456–470.

———, 1959. *Die Phylogenie der Pflanzen*, 2nd ed., Stuttgart: Gustav Fischer.

chapter eight ❯❯❯❯❯ Seed Plants

Although fossil plants with anatomical characters suggesting a seed plant affinity are known in the Devonian period, the first seedlike structure is not known in rocks older than Lower Carboniferous. The fact that a plant with gymnospermous wood such as that found in *Archaeopteris* may actually be an arborescent fern makes it difficult to conclude, on the basis of vegetative anatomy only, the affinities of certain fossils. Admittedly, the seed habit might have originated in the Devonian period, and it actually may have originated more than once in different groups of plants.

The origin of a seedlike structure can only be hypothesized, but recent paleobotanical findings shed some light on the problem. Morphologically a seed[1] is a modified sporangium with one functional megaspore and with an integumentary system. *Lepidocarpon* would fit this definition, and although it is not exactly homologous with seeds of gymnosperms and angiosperms, it certainly functioned like a seed. Thus, in the evolution of a seed, one necessary step would be the evolution of heterospory from a primitive homosporous condition. This heterospory may not necessarily have been based on a difference in the sizes of spores, but simply on a difference in function. Ultimately, only one functional megaspore is left as a result of a progressive loss of spores in the mega-

---

[1] It is customary to speak of fossil ovules as "seeds" even though an embryo may not be present. Strictly speaking, the term "ovule" would be more appropriate for most of the seedlike structures in the Paleozoic and, in certain instances, in the Mesozoic.

sporangium. This functional megaspore was retained in the megasporangium, and the megagametophyte developed within the spore.
One or more archegonia were produced by the gametophyte.

Around the sporangium was developed an integumentary system of some kind. In *Lepidocarpon* and *Miadesmia* the integumentary system was developed from the modified sporophyll, parts of
which enveloped the sporangium, leaving an opening (micropyle)
where the sporophyll flaps did not completely enclose the entire
sporangium. Although it is not known for certain, it seems probable
that the embryo developed within the enclosed gametophyte. The
megagametophyte in *Lepidocarpon* was relatively bulky and could
have functioned as endosperm for the developing embryo.

Seeds of other groups of plants probably had a different origin
from that of seedlike structures among the Lycopsida. Similar to
Lepidocarpon was the development of a sporangium with one
functional megaspore[2] in which developed the gametophyte. The
integumentary system had a different origin, however. There is no
structure in the seed plants comparable to the sporophyll of the
Lycopsida. The integument must have originated in a different
way.

Some recent discoveries are of considerable significance in this
connection. *Genomosperma* is a Lower Carboniferous seedlike body
borne on a slender, elongated pedicel (Fig. 8-1A). The nucellus, or
megasporangium, terminates this stalk but it is subtended in
G. Kidstoni by a whorl of eight elongated processes that form an
open cup around the nucellus. The length of these processes is about
twice that of the nucellus. At the distal end the nucellus is modified
into a pollen-receiving structure; the nucellus is open distally, and
just within the opening is a small mass of parenchyma tissue.

Technically speaking *Genomosperma* is still a naked sporangium that is incompletely covered by an integument. The etymology
of the genus name is appropriate in this instance ($\gamma i \gamma \nu o \mu \alpha \iota$ — "to
become," and $\sigma \pi \acute{\epsilon} \rho \mu \alpha$ — "seed"). No distinct micropyle is present, but
rather pollen landed directly on the distal tip of the nucellus.

A second species, *G. latens*, is somewhat more advanced than

---

[2] It is recognized that certain ovules may have more than one functional
megaspore. The "normal" pattern, however, might be regarded as the type
with only one megaspore.

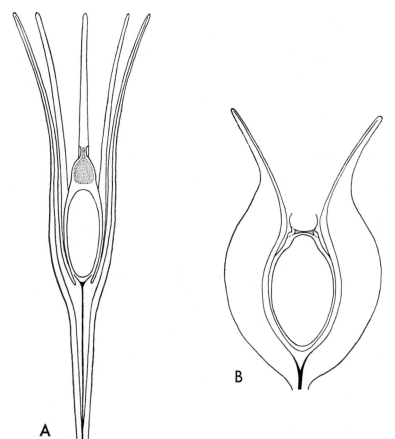

Fig. 8-1. A, diagrammatic longitudinal section of *Genomosperma Kidstoni* with the nucellus loosely surrounded by elongated sterile appendages. (Slightly modified from Long, 1960a.) B, diagrammatic longitudinal section of *Lyrasperma scotica*. Note exposed distal end of the nucellus. (Redrawn from Long, 1960b.)

G. Kidstoni. In *G. latens* the eight integumentary processes are more closely appressed to the nucellus, and although they are separate structures for most of their lengths, there is partial fusion of these structures to each other around the very base of the nucellus. In this respect, *G. latens* more closely approximates a seed.

Those who argue that *Lepidocarpon* cannot be called a seed will have to agree that *Genomosperma* does not fit into that category either. Both genera, however, are significant in showing the conversion of a naked sporangium into a definite seedlike structure.

Lyrasperma is a bilaterally flattened seed, also from the Lower Carboniferous (Fig. 8-1B). A section of the seed parallel with the flat face has a certain resemblance to a lyre: the integument is fused to the nucellus except at the very tip where two halves of the integument are free from the sporangium and extend outward some distance beyond the tip of the nucellus. The tip of the nucellus is still exposed to falling pollen grains, but considerably more of the nucellus is enveloped by the integument than in *Genomosperma*.

A more nearly typical seed would have a nucellus even more completely covered by the integument, with only a small micropyle through which pollen might enter the ovule.

These studies of Lower Carboniferous seeds are significant in helping to interpret the morphology of the integument. In at least some gymnospermous seeds the integument appears to have been derived from sterile appendages borne below the nucellus or sporangium. These sterile appendages first formed a cuplike structure around the sporangium, but the individual processes were separate. Next, fusion of these sterile members occurred, beginning first at the base and gradually extending more distally. Perhaps the earliest type of integument was one that left the tip of the nucellus exposed and in which there was no fusion to the sporangium. Subsequently, more complete integumentary fusion with the sporangium occurred, and only a small micropyle was left distally.

Some pteridosperm seeds have integuments with more than one distinct zone. These regions might conceivably represent a specialization of the enveloping processes such as found in *Genomosperma*, or they might be the result of a fusion of a second or even a third set of appendages around the first. In fact, it is possible that both of these modifications may actually have occurred.

These remarks concerning the possible evolution of certain seeds are tenable in light of the existing seeds and seed precursors. The actual groups that may have played an important part in the evolution of seed plants have not yet been demonstrated convincingly, however. Some of the seed ferns, probably representing the most primitive kinds of seed plants, have certain characteristics of ferns and others of more typical gymnospermous plants. However, the fernlike habit of some of these plants does not necessarily mean that they were derived from true ferns. It is conceivable, indeed quite probable, that seed ferns developed contemporaneously with true ferns. Certain of the Devonian fernlike plants have anatomical features suggestive of pteridosperm vegetative structure, but they are definitely cryptogamous in their reproduction. If the suggested origin of the integumentary system of a seed fern seed is to mean anything, one must look to plants that had not yet attained the fern level of evolution. The sterile processes surrounding the nucellus must have been more nearly "telomic" than leaflike. Nevertheless, there existed in the Devonian certain groups of plants, such as some of the Aneurophytales and the Cladoxylales, that may have had some relationship with pteridosperm ancestors, if not with the seed ferns themselves.

The coexistence of conifers or coniferlike plants with the seed ferns might suggest that the two groups may have originated independently. Certain structural features of conifer vegetative and reproductive anatomy resemble corresponding features in the pteridosperms, yet there are enough differences that might have been accounted for by a long period of separation of the two groups, or even by separate origins. In some respects it is easier to follow a telomic origin of the reproductive and vegetative structures of early conifers rather than to derive these structures from seed fern characters. Nevertheless, the homologies that do exist between the two groups of seed plants cannot be dismissed.

REFERENCES

ANDREWS, H. N., JR., 1961. "Heterospory and the evolution of the seed" (in Andrews, H. N., Jr., 1961. *Studies in Paleobotany*, New York: John Wiley & Sons, Inc., 364–379).

EAMES, A. J., 1955. "The seed and *Ginkgo*," *J. Arnold Arb.*, **36**: 165–170.

LONG, A. G., 1960a. "On the structure of *Calymmatotheca Kidstoni* Calder (emended) and *Genomosperma latens* gen. et sp. nov. from the Calciferous Sandstone series of Berwickshire," *Trans. Roy. Soc. Edinburgh*, **64**: 29–44.

———, 1960b. "On the structure of *Samaropsis scotica* Calder (emended) and *Eurostoma angulare* gen. et sp. nov., petrified seeds from the Calciferous Sandstone series of Berwickshire," *Trans. Roy. Soc. Edinburgh*, **64**: 261–280.

WALTON, J., 1953. "The evolution of the ovule in the pteridosperms," *Adv. Sci. London*, **10**: 223–230.

chapter nine

▸▸▸▸▸ Subdivision

Pteropsida, Class

Cycadophyta

Traditionally, the seed plants are grouped into two classes -- the Gymnospermae, or naked seeded plants, and the Angiospermae, which generally have seeds that are enclosed. Recent morphological and paleobotanical investigations, however, seem to suggest that the gymnosperms are not really a natural group, and the fact that all have naked seeds is not a sufficient criterion for setting up such a group. Cycads and cycad relatives are quite different from the conifers, which, in turn, are different from the Gnetales and other gymnospermous plants. It might be better, then, to use the term "gymnosperm" as a descriptive one, and one not necessarily implying relationships among all plants included in this category.

Modern morphologists and paleobotanists recognize at least three, and sometimes more, classes of gymnospermous plants. Each class represents a group of plants equal in magnitude to the class Pterophyta or to the class of flowering plants, the Angiospermophyta (or Angiospermae). One class of gymnospermous plants that seems to be a fairly natural one is the Cycadophyta.

Most of the Cycadophyta have large, frondlike leaves that are petiolate and that generally have a leathery texture. Even compressions of fossil cycadophyte leaves suggest that the leaves were thick and coriaceous in life. Traces supplying these leaves are either few in number and large, or many in number and small. Secondary vascular tissues are usually present, and most often the tracheids are large and thin-walled; much parenchyma, in the form of many and often large vascular rays, gives the wood a "loose" appearance as opposed to the generally compact wood of conifers. Finally, pollen-bearing organs and seeds are borne on specialized leaves that may be relatively unmodified or quite specialized.

Within the class Cycadophyta are at least three orders: Pteridospermales, Cycadeoidales, and Cycadales. Only the Cycadales have living representatives; the other two orders became extinct in the Mesozoic.

PTERIDOSPERMALES

Although no seeds are known in the Devonian period, the origin of the pteridosperms is generally placed in that period, and the order extended to the Jurassic. In general habit, the seed ferns resembled certain tree ferns with large, frondlike leaves. Seeds and microsporangia were borne on leaves, and in some cases these reproductive structures took the place of pinnules on the frond. Pteridosperm seeds were very similar to those in modern cycads, and microsporangiate organs generally lacked annuli and not infrequently were synangiate.

Paleozoic pteridosperms are often classified into three families: the Lyginopteridaceae, Medullosaceae, and Calamopityaceae.

Lyginopteridaceae

Lyginopteris oldhamia, an Upper Carboniferous stem genus, is the first stem to have been shown to possess pteridospermous affinities (Fig. 9-1A). In fact, in 1904 the investigations of leaves and reproductive organs belonging to this stem conclusively demonstrated the existence of such a group as the pteridosperms.

The stem of *L. oldhamia* has a central parenchymatous pith in which are scattered nests of what appear to be sclerotic cells. Primary xylem occurs at the periphery of the pith in the form of several prominent mesarch bundles. Secondary xylem, generally just a few millimeters thick, has large, circular bordered pitted tracheids and numerous rays. Outside of the secondary phloem is a "pericyclic" layer that also has sclerotic nests similar to those

Fig. 9-1. A, transverse section of a stem of *Lyginopteris oldhamia*. B, cross section of a large stem of *Heterangium americanum*. C, *Callistophyton poroxyloides*, stem cross section.

in the pith. It is in this layer that periderm begins to develop. The inner primary cortex is parenchymatous with thin walls, and the outer cortex has a characteristic network of fibrous cells that form a regular anastomosing system. In the interstices are thin-walled parenchyma cells. In a cross section of the stem, the fibrous network appears as a number of radiating dark lines, not unlike the Roman numerals on a clock face. At the surface of young stems are stalked capitate glands with cells in the head that appear to have broken down into a mucilaginous or resinous material.

Leaf traces originate from the primary xylem bundles as a result of the tangential splitting of each bundle. One of the resulting strands continues upward in the stem, while the other bends outward and upward, passing through the secondary xylem and becoming double outside of the xylem. These two traces reunite in the petiole and form a V- or W-shaped petiole trace.

The leaves, petrified remains of which are known, were large compound fronds with lobed pinnules that were constricted at their attachment (similar to *Sphenopteris Hoeninghausi,* a common compression form). The main rachis forked dichotomously once, and the rest of the frond was divided pinnately. Of considerable interest is the presence of a fibrous outer cortical network in the petiole like that in the stem. In addition, capitate glands were borne on the petiole and smaller rachises.

The work of Oliver and Scott, two British paleobotanists, on the seed *Lagenostoma Lomaxi* was of considerable significance in the interpretation of *Lyginopteris oldhamia.* The seed is small and barrel-shaped, about 5.5 mm long and 4.25 mm wide. The integument is fused to the nucellus except at the very tip where the nucellus is prolonged into a flask-shaped structure that projects into the micropyle (compare the related *L. ovoides* in Fig. 9-4A). The flask-like chamber is not completely hollow, but a solid core of thin-walled parenchyma projects into it leaving a pollen chamber between the core of parenchyma and the wall of the "flask." Indeed, pollen grains have been found in some *Lagenostoma* pollen chambers.

Although *Lagenostoma Lomaxi* is a naked seed, it was borne within a cupulate structure shaped somewhat like a tulip. It was a fused cup with a lobed edge. On the outer surface of this cupule were attached capitate glands of the same kind as those found on

Lyginopteris oldhamia stems and on the leaf fragments attached to these stems. Oliver and Scott concluded that *L. Lomaxi* must have been the seed attached to the plant that had stems assigned to *Lyginopteris oldhamia,* and they thereby demonstrated the existence of an unusual group of plants, the seed ferns.

Paleobotanists had long suspected that such a group must have existed, but there had been no definite proof before the work of Oliver and Scott. In fact, those who worked with compressed Paleozoic fern leaves were impressed by the fact that certain genera and species of leaves were never found with sporangia on them, and thus some of these paleobotanists began to doubt that these leaves were actually parts of fern fronds.

After the discovery of Oliver and Scott, more seed genera were assigned to pteridosperm stem genera, and there were many examples of actual attachment of seeds to fernlike leaves. The term "Age of Ferns," so often applied to the Carboniferous period, may not be an accurate description of that time because many of these "ferns" really represent leaves of gymnospermous plants.

Roots, leaves, and seeds associated with *Lyginopteris* are all well known, but the pollen-bearing structure has not yet been definitely assigned to this plant. One possible contender is the genus *Crossotheca,* also borne on *Sphenopteris* foliage, the tip members of which were modified into the pollen-bearing regions. Some of the distal pinnules were flattened, and from one face many elongated sporangia projected downward in parallel arrangement along the periphery. The pinnule with its sporangia had the general appearance of a hairbrush or of an epaulet. If *Crossotheca* is indeed the microsporangiate structure borne by *Lyginopteris,* it is difficult to explain the not infrequent occurrence of the former genus in this country, and no substantiated report of the stem genus in the western hemisphere.

A more simple type of pteridosperm stem, and one that might best be used as the starting point for a discussion of evolution of pteridosperm stelar types, is *Heterangium,* a widespread Carboniferous genus (Fig. 9-1B). *Heterangium* stems are small and are protostelic; the primary xylem is a mixture of clusters of rather large tracheids and an abundance of parenchyma cells. The general appearance of the primary xylem of *Heterangium,* in fact, is reminiscent of the stele of *Gleichenia,* a fern frequently used to demonstrate a protostele. Primary xylem is mesarch, with the protoxylem slightly embedded in the metaxylem near the periphery of the xylem rod. Secondary xylem was produced in varying amounts; some specimens have no secondary wood while others may have a centimeter or more. Often the wood is separated into wedges in cross section by wide rays. Secondary xylem tracheids are smaller than those in the primary xylem, and metaxylem and secondary tracheids have many circular bordered pits on the walls. Phloem is often preserved, and in certain species a cross section of the phloem reveals wedge-shaped regions separated by flaring rays. This configuration resembles the cross section of *Tilia*, the linden, and one species of *Heterangium* has even been called *H. tiliaeoides* because of this resemblance.

Leaf traces may start singly at their points of separation from the primary xylem, or they may be double strands from the beginning. In the inner cortex the trace is double, and each strand may divide further before the series of traces enters the petiole base.

The inner cortex is parenchymatous except for horizontal plates of sclerotic cells; in the outer cortex are vertically aligned bundles of sclerenchyma.

Fronds of *Heterangium* are thought to have been of the *Sphenopteris* type. In fact, certain compression species of *Sphenopteris* show horizontal bands of more resistant tissue that might correspond to the sclerenchyma plates in the cortex of *Heterangium*.

The structure of the stem of *Heterangium* shows a condition that could have been the precursor of the anatomy of *Lyginopteris*. In a stem such as that of *H. Grievii* from the Lower Carboniferous, the primary xylem is fairly uniform in size and distribution of tracheids except for somewhat smaller elements near the edge of the protostele. In a form such as the Upper Carboniferous species *H. Andrei*, the tracheids in the center of the protostele are less compactly organized, with a predominance of parenchyma. The more compact peripheral xylem strands are fewer in number than are usually found in *Heterangium* and are quite distinct. Also in this species, a single leaf trace splits into two in the cortex. A complete conversion of the center part of the stele in a plant such as *H. Andrei* to a pith would result in a structure quite similar to that in *Lyginopteris*.

Fruiting structures of *Heterangium* are even less certain than they are in *Lyginopteris*. One seed, *Sphaerostoma ovale*, possibly belongs to *H. Grievii*. Like *Lagenostoma*, *Sphaerostoma* has a cupule that does not flare, but is closely pressed around the seed itself. Also, as in *Lagenostoma*, the integument is fused to the nucellus except at the very tip where the nucellus is modified into a short, squat column of parenchyma cells surrounded by a hollow, doughnut-shaped chamber. This circular hollow region is the pollen chamber, and the pollen grains enter it when the inner edge of the circular ring is separated from the solid nucellar projection. The integument has papillate projections and is lobed at the distal end. Except in particulars, *Sphaerostoma* and *Lagenostoma* are strikingly similar.

Sphaerostoma does not occur in North America, and because *Heterangium* stems occur not uncommonly, American workers have attempted to determine whether other seed genera might have affinities with *Heterangium*. One of these is the genus *Conostoma*, a rather small, elongated, and generally radially symmetrical seed (Fig. 9-4B). It too has a fused integument and nucellus, and as in *Sphaerostoma*, a hollow, ring-shaped pollen chamber surrounds a central nucellar projection that in *Conostoma* is hollow. *Physostoma* is similarly constructed, with a fused nucellus and integument except at the distal end where the integument is extended into about ten projections. Externally, the integument is covered with large, swollen, hairlike structures. The pollen chamber is somewhat simpler than that in seeds just mentioned. In *Physostoma* the pollen chamber is a hollow flask-shaped structure that fits around the distal nucellar end.

Although *Lyginopteris* is absent from rocks in this country, there is a genus closely approximating it in many respects. This is the Upper Pennsylvanian *Callistophyton*, which has a pith containing scattered secretory cells and surrounded by a number of mesarch primary xylem strands (Fig. 9-1C). These strands are not as pronounced as they are in *Lyginopteris*. In some of these strands there is but one protoxylem group; others may have two. Leaf traces originate from these strands as they do in *Lyginopteris*, and four protoxylem groups are present in a leaf trace as it bends outward and upward from the periphery of the pith. Typical pteridospermous secondary wood is present, composed of circular bordered pitted tracheids and conspicuous vascular rays. Secondary phloem contains rays, phloem parenchyma cells, and well-preserved sieve cells in which remains of sieve plates are visible. Outside the inner portion of the cortex, which is parenchymatous with secretory cells, is a peripheral system of elongated fiberlike cells somewhat similar to that in *Lyginopteris* but not so pronounced. At the surface of the stem are capitate multicellular hairs. Periderm is initiated in the cortex, and in older stems the outer part of the cortex was sloughed off and the periderm became the external limiting layer. As leaf traces progressed upward and outward they expanded tangentially, and in the leaf base and petiole the vascular bundle is a flat strand. Pinna traces arose from the lateral edges of this strand.

A study of the apical region of *Callistophyton poroxyloides* shows that the leaves were frondlike with circinate vernation. These frondlike leaves were at least twice compound.

No specimen of *Callistophyton* has been seen with seeds attached, and its assignment to the pteridosperms is based on the presence of fernlike leaves and similarity of its vegetative anatomy to that of *Lyginopteris*. The former feature, of course, does not preclude its assignment to the true ferns, although this position would seem unlikely.

Schopfiastrum decussatum is a small protostelic pteridosperm stem from the Middle Pennsylvanian. Tracheids and parenchyma make up the central part of the stem, but the amount of parenchyma is somewhat less than that in a *Heterangium* protostele. Secondary wood is also present. The outer part of the cortex in cross section shows radially elongated strands of sclerenchyma fibers that do not anastomose as they do in *Lyginopteris*. Leaf arrangement, as the specific name suggests, appears to have been in four rows, with the two members of a pair not quite opposite. Leaf traces were large and tangentially expanded, not unlike those in *Callistophyton*.

Another unusual plant from the Middle Pennsylvanian, *Microspermopteris,* has a stele very much like that of *Heterangium*. Small clusters of metaxylem tracheids, 12 to 14 in number, are separated by a thin network of parenchyma. Secondary wood is present, although not abundant, and has small tracheids and rays. The outer cortex has a series of horizontal sclerotic plates, another feature found in *Heterangium*. No leaves are known, but the surface of the stem bears multicellular spinelike emergences.

A clue concerning the possible origin of certain monostelic pteridosperms such as those in the Lyginopteridaceae lies in *Tetrastichia bupatides*, a Lower Carboniferous pteridosperm. This plant had a slender stem, with long internodes, and leaves were borne decussately. The primary xylem as seen in cross section was a solid strand with four arms. Secondary xylem was also present. In the middle cortex are sclerotic nests, while the outer cortex shows a network of sclerenchyma fibers. A swelling is present on the petiole where it is attached to the stem, and petioles bifurcated about five inches from their points of attachment. No leaves, roots, or reproductive structures are known.

Anatomically, the stem is fernlike, and as W. T. Gordon, who described *Tetrastichia*, writes: "Had the stem of *Tetrastichia* been found in a decorticated condition, and without secondary wood, it would certainly have been classed with the ferns." In fact, *Tetrastichia* is more fernlike than any other of the Lyginopteridaceae. The Upper Devonian, fernlike *Tetraxylopteris* has certain features in common with *Tetrastichia*, and it is conceivable that pteridosperms originated from a complex of such plants that are fernlike, yet that cannot without difficulty be classified among the true ferns.

It is primarily because of the cortical characters of *Tetrastichia*, which include sclerotic nests and the fibrous network, in addition to the petiole characters, which resemble those of *Lyginopteris*, that *Tetrastichia* is included with the seed ferns rather than with the ferns.

Medullosaceae

A second family of Paleozoic pteridosperms, the Medullosaceae, is complex, with unusual stem types. Unlike the monostelic Lyginopteridaceae, the Medullosaceae have polystelic stems, often with a large number of individual steles at a given level. If there is such a thing as a "typical" *Medullosa*, it might be considered to be *M. Noei* at a level with three steles (Fig. 9-2A). These steles are elongated in cross section, and the primary xylem consists of large tracheids and an abundance of thin-walled parenchyma. Protoxylem is near the edge of each stele that faces the outside of the stem. Except for

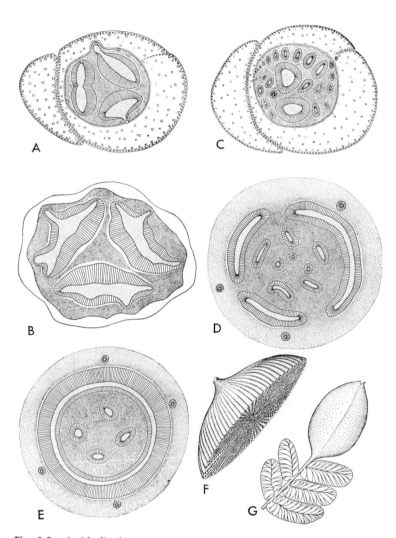

Fig. 9-2. A, idealized transverse section of a young, three-steled stem of a typical Carboniferous *Medullosa* such as *M. Noei*. B, diagrammatic transverse section of a fairly old stem portion of *Medullosa Noei*. Outer cortical tissues have sloughed off and a thick zone of periderm is the external limiting layer. C, diagrammatic transverse section of a polystelic *Medullosa* such as *M. primaeva*. D, idealized cross section of *M. Leuckarti*. E, diagrammatic cross section of *M. stellata*. F, reconstruction of *Dolerotheca formosa*. G, restoration of a large pteridosperm seed attached to *Neuropteris* foliage. (A, C–E, and G, redrawn from Stewart and Delevoryas, 1956; F, modified from Stewart and Delevoryas, 1956.)

the lack of radial symmetry, each primary xylem body of a *Medullosa* stele is quite similar to that of a *Heterangium* stele. Secondary tracheids surround the primary xylem, and there are many vascular rays. Not infrequently there is more secondary xylem development toward the center of the stem than there is toward the outside. Secondary phloem surrounds the xylem, and the steles are embedded in a mass of thin-walled ground tissue that often contains secretory cells or canals. A massive cortex, marked by prominent peripheral fibrous strands and many scattered leaf traces, surrounds the steles. These traces arise from the steles at various levels, and many are present at one level of the cortex. Secretory canals are also frequent in the cortex, especially toward the outside. Deep within the cortex, just outside of the cluster of steles, periderm development was initiated, and even in very young stems, there is a thin band of internal periderm. Just below the level of separation of a leaf from the stem, a series of sclerotic strands cut through the cortex marking the position of separation of the leaf base. A considerable portion of the cortex is cut off to form the leaf base. Leaves had a more or less helical arrangement on the stem.

Many changes occurred at a given level of a *Medullosa* stem as it grew older. Later, the steles were larger, the cortex sloughed off, and the periderm, which had become much thicker, became the outer limiting layer. These maturation stages are not as simple as they are in many plants that have secondary growth. Not only is the secondary xylem thicker at an older stage, but the primary xylem is also considerably larger (Fig. 9-2B). Of course there is no way to demonstrate that primary xylem increases in size as steles get larger, but in almost every case (and many specimens have been examined), when the primary xylem is small, there is only a small amount of secondary xylem. When the secondary wood is thick, it is always found in association with large primary xylem strands. The probable explanation of this correlation lies in the nature of the primary xylem, which has a great amount of parenchyma. It appears that the parenchymalike cells in the primary xylem retained their ability to divide — that is, they were probably persistent procambium — and produced more cells as the stem matured, some of which differentiated into tracheids, while others remained thin-walled. The shape of an old stele in cross section seems to support this idea. It is somewhat elongated, ideally elliptical, with less secondary xylem formed at the edges of the stele than near the middle, suggesting that the cambium had been functioning for a shorter period of time at the edges. This would happen if the steles expanded, especially tangentially. It is certain that the parenchymalike tissue within the primary xylem did indeed retain its ability to divide, for in many old steles of *M. Noei,* cylinders of secondary parenchyma, results of proliferation of living cells, were produced within the primary xylem.

One might expect that in older stems, with abundant secondary xylem and phloem, the secondary vascular tissues would abut on each other at the center of the stem. Surprisingly enough, however, in older stems the steles are actually farther apart than they are in young stems. This phenomenon is again explainable on the basis of meristematic activity of parenchymalike cells, this time in the ground tissue. Here, too, in old stems, there are sometimes cylinders of secondary peridermlike tissue produced by a proliferation of the cells in the ground tissue, although presumably most of the meristematic activity was not in regular planes.

In *M. Noei* it appears that any living cell had the capacity to divide, and there was often proliferation of cells in various regions. Even ray parenchyma cells sometimes proliferated, thus producing masses of secondary parenchyma within the secondary wood.

The external limiting periderm, which began deep within the cortex, did not develop from a phellogen, but it seems that here, too, cells in the periderm were living and simply proliferated.

Medullosa primaeva is an example of a species that has many steles at certain levels and that underwent the same kinds of maturation stages as *M. Noei,* although there was somewhat less proliferation of parenchyma cells in *M. primaeva* (Fig. 9-2C). At certain levels of the stem there may be only two steles that may branch considerably at higher levels to form 20 or more steles. Still higher there are anastomoses, and again a small number of steles may be present. Some of the branch steles bend outward into the cortex and become leaf traces; at their lower levels they are indistinguishable from stem steles, however. Old stems of *M. primaeva* also have large steles, tangentially expanded, with larger primary bodies and more secondary development.

Roots of *Medullosa* are protostelic, generally tetrarch, and are adventitious.

Petioles of *Medullosa* when found isolated are called *Myeloxylon,* and they have an amazing superficial resemblance to a large monocotyledonous stem. There are many scattered vascular bundles, and near the periphery of the petiole are sclerenchyma fiber strands like those in the cortex of the stem. There are also many secretory canals. The more proximal branching of the frond rachis is dichotomous, with unequal branching found more distally. Fronds were of the *Alethopteris* and *Neuropteris* types (see Fig. 9-4F, G).

One could reasonably assume that the forms having many steles are the primitive types of *Medullosa,* and those having a small number of steles that seldom branched or anastomosed, such as *M. Noei,* are more advanced. Another line of development could also have led from the polystelic Carboniferous types to many of the European Permian species. *Medullosa Leuckarti* has a few peripheral steles that are considerably expanded tangentially (Fig. 9-2D). Internal to these steles are a number of smaller steles. *Medullosa stellata* may represent a stelar type that could have been derived from the *M. Leuckarti* type of structure. A tangential fusion (phylogenetically) of the peripheral steles would result in a continuous cylinder with a ring of primary xylem and both centripetal and centrifugal secondary xylem. *Medullosa stellata* has this kind of structure with several smaller steles within the large, outer one (Fig. 9-2E).

Seeds of the medullosan pteridosperms are considerably larger than those borne by members of the Lyginopteridaceae. *Pachytesta,* a rather abundant genus of petrified seeds (Fig. 9-4D, E), is a typical example. It has a sclerotesta (that may not actually have been sclerotic) with three prominent ribs. Surrounding this layer is a softer coat, the sarcotesta. Within the integuments, the nucellus is attached to the seed coats only at its base; otherwise it is separate. At the distal end of the nucellus is a hollow pollen chamber, much more simple than nucellar modifications in seeds discussed previously. It is simply a hollow region with a small distal opening through which pollen grains entered. In some species of *Pachytesta,* the sclerotesta is relatively unornamented, with only three major ribs. Other species may have secondary ribs between the major ones, and in one species there may be more than 30 of these smaller ribs. No embryos have been found in these seeds (nor in any other Paleozoic seed), but gametophytes occasionally are preserved with archegonia and egg cells.

In some instances compressed seeds of the approximate dimensions and general external configuration of *Pachytesta* are found attached to fronds of *Neuropteris* (Fig. 9-2G). In these specimens the seed takes the place of a terminal or lateral pinnule.

Casts of large seeds are also frequent. These sandstone bodies have three prominent ribs (much like the shape of a *Ginkgo* seed sclerotesta, with three ribs instead of two) that probably correspond to the internal contours of the sclerotesta of a seed such as *Pachytesta*. Some of these sandstone casts go under the name of *Trigonocarpus*.

Stephanospermum, three-angled in cross section in some species, is another seed that may belong to the medullosan pteridosperms. Distally, the sclerotesta is elongated into a beaklike structure, and a short distance back there is a secondary crownlike flange of the sclerotesta (hence the name *Stephanospermum*) that is also directed distally (Fig. 9-4C).

Several genera of pollen-bearing organs are thought to have been possible medullosan microsporangia. All of these are relatively large structures, and generally synangiate.

Codonotheca is an urn-shaped structure with free, fingerlike projections at the edge of the small cup. These projections are actually tubular sporangia, with large pollen grains. The grains are of the *Monoletes* type, having a single furrow.

If a *Codonotheca*-type of synangium with many sporangia could be imagined to have produced a larger, urn-shaped structure with sporangia fused laterally around a central hollow region, a structure such as *Whittleseya* would be the result (Fig. 9-4H). *Whittleseya* also has large, monolete pollen grains. *Whittleseya* is known from compressions and has been found attached to *Neuropteris* foliage. One synangium takes the place of a single pinnule in these compressed fossils.

Aulacotheca is also a synangium with several tubular sporangia, but it is not open distally (Fig. 9-5C). It is elongated, ellipsoid, with a central cavity and a single layer of sporangia fused laterally.

Boulaya is very similar to *Aulacotheca*, but rather than having

Fig. 9-3. Suggested reconstruction of a plant of *Medullosa Noei* about 15 feet tall. (From Stewart and Delevoryas, 1956.)

many tubular sporangia, the sporogenous region was continuous laterally.

Goldenbergia was borne in a single series along a pinna axis, and each synangium is essentially like an *Aulacotheca* synangium, but not quite so elongated (Fig. 9-5A, B).

The elongate *Thuringia* is a solid synangiate organ with a number of long, slender sporangia (Fig. 9-5D).

In *Potoniea,* a massive microsporangiate structure, there is a shallow, campanulate cupule within which are hundreds of elongated, tubular sporangia. *Dolerotheca* has the same shape, but the many elongated sporangia are fused within a sterile campanulum (Fig. 9-2F). Furthermore, in cross section the sporangia appear as circles in radiating paired rows.

Although it is difficult to place these several genera into a precise evolutionary line, it is obvious that there is a relationship among them and that all show specialization based on a central theme. It is not unreasonable to assume that the primitive condition among medullosan pteridosperm microsporangiate organs would be a three-dimensional branching cluster with separate, elongated sporangia. Fusion of these at the base, with the tips left free, would result in a *Codonotheca*-type of synangium. If these free sporangia in the primitive hypothetical branch system fused laterally with a central hollow, *Whittleseya* and *Aulacotheca* and others would be the logical results. A tight fusion of a large number of such sporangia would closely resemble *Dolerotheca*. In fact, the vascularization of the campanulum of *Dolerotheca* is conspicuously dichotomously branched, suggesting that a dichotomous branch system was the original situation.

A reconstruction of a Carboniferous *Medullosa,* then, would show an unbranched stem with a rough, periderm-covered stem below and a number of prop roots near the base of the stem (Fig. 9-3). Higher up the erect stem is sloughing cortex and leaf bases, and still higher, large, compound fronds are borne in a terminal crown. Some of the fronds bear large seeds in place of pinnules, while on other fronds (it is not known whether on the same tree or not) are synangiate structures. Among the American medullosas, *Dolerotheca* and *Pachytesta* would be the most common fruiting structures.

In many respects, the medullosan pteridosperms are an un-

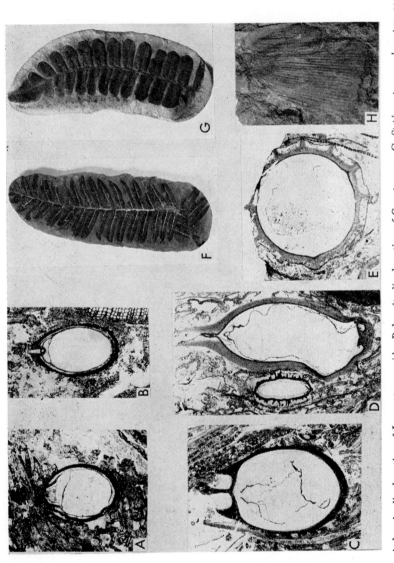

Fig. 9-4. A, longitudinal section of *Lagenostoma ovoides*. B, longitudinal section of *Conostoma* sp. C, *Stephanospermum elongatum*, sectioned longitudinally. D, *Pachytesta composita*, longitudinal section. Note sectioned specimen of *Cardiocarpus spinatus* to the left (see Chapter 11). (From Stewart, 1958.) E, transverse section of *Pachytesta composita*. (From Stewart, 1958.) F, compression of *Alethopteris*-type

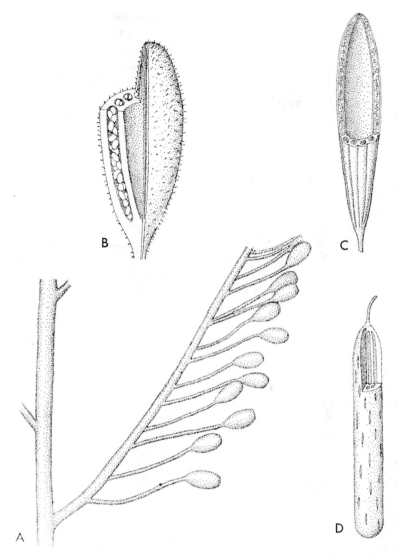

Fig. 9-5. A, part of the fertile frond of *Goldenbergia glomerata*. B, diagrammatic reconstruction of a synangium cut open to show sporangia and spores. C, restoration of the synangium of *Aulacotheca elongata* cut open to expose sporangia and spores. (A–C redrawn from Halle, 1933.) D, reconstruction of *Thuringia callipteroides* with a portion cut away to show interior of synangium. (Redrawn from Remy, 1953.)

usual group of plants, without parallel in modern floras. Certain modern plants are polystelic at maturity, but this condition is derived as a result of aberrant cambial activity, resulting in secondary xylem and phloem in the form of several distinct units. In young stages, there is still one primary portion of a stele. Medullosans were polystelic throughout (although, admittedly, it is not known what the seedling may have looked like). Another unusual feature is the expanding primary xylem and ground tissue due to proliferation of parenchymalike cells in the primary xylem and in the tissue between the steles.

One reason it has been suggested that the species of *Medullosa* having many steles are primitive is that there is difficulty in distinguishing between steles and leaf traces in those forms. In other words, leaves at their basal regions resemble stems with many steles. In fact, a *Medullosa primaeva* specimen has been discovered that has a branch with three steles; these three steles have secondary wood near the base of the lateral branch and originate just as do leaf traces with secondary wood. Externally, it would be impossible to distinguish between leaf and branch.

A suggested scheme of evolution of the medullosans begins with a dichotomously branched, psilophytic plant, followed by a similar type with secondary vascular tissues. A next step would be a persistent dichotomy of stelar axes, but a fusion of cortices of the individual axes, resulting in a polystelic construction. Next would have occurred anastomosis and a progressive reduction in the number of steles. There would also have been a progressive differentiation between stem steles and leaf traces.

Some of the Cladoxylales and related forms may have a bearing on the origin of *Medullosa*. Many of the forms in that order (for example, *Cladoxylon taeniatum* and *Voelkelia refracta*) have many steles with secondary vascular development.

Xenocladia medullosina, a related Upper Devonian species, is polystelic, with peripheral radiating steles surrounding central, more nearly cylindrical, ones. It is probably closer to being a fern than a pteridosperm and has a vegetative structure like that of the Cladoxylales. In fact, the most promising ancestral types to the pteridosperms appear to lie in the group of late Devonian-early Mississippian forms about which more needs to be known concerning foliage and reproductive structures.

Calamopityaceae

A third family of Paleozoic pteridosperms, the Calamopityaceae, is an artificial one and serves as a catchall for certain stem types that do not fit into any of the other groups. These types are all monostelic as are the Lyginopteridaceae, but, in general, the secondary wood is more compact.

Stenomyelon, from the late Devonian-early Carboniferous, is protostelic, with a three-lobed, massive, exarch primary xylem strand surrounded by secondary wood that is cylindrical in outline (Fig. 9-6A). Leaf traces separate from the edges of the primary xylem arms, bifurcate at a higher level, and further divide higher in the cortex. The outer cortex has a radiating, anastomosing network of fibrous cells.

Calamopitys, of similar age, has a pith, but scattered among the parenchyma cells are occasional isolated tracheids (Fig. 9-6B). The bulk of the primary xylem is in the form of mesarch bundles at the periphery of the pith. Secondary xylem is also present in this genus, and the stele is embedded within a massive cortex. Radiating bands of sclerenchyma cells are found near the periphery of the cortex. At the level of origin of a leaf trace, one of the primary xylem groups divides to form two in radial file; the outer one is the leaf trace, and the inner is the reparatory strand. Farther up and outward, the trace becomes double and divides again at a higher level. *Kalymma* is the name given to isolated petioles that probably belong to *Calamopitys* and related genera. In many respects *Kalymma* resembles *Myeloxylon,* the petiole belonging to medullosan pteridosperms.

Diichnia kentuckiensis is an American member of the Calamopityaceae and has many features in common with *Calamopitys* (Fig. 9-6C). In *Diichnia,* as in *Calamopitys,* the pith has scattered tracheids. Primary xylem is in the form of mesarch bundles that are separated from the secondary xylem by parenchyma. The pith is five-angled, with primary xylem strands situated in these angles. Leaf traces are double from their point of origin; two primary xylem strands in adjacent angles divide, the inner members becoming reparatory strands and the outer ones representing leaf traces. In the cortex, the leaf traces expand tangentially and divide, forming a C-shaped group of bundles.

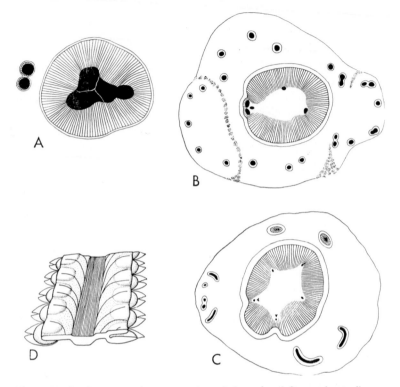

Fig. 9-6. A, diagrammatic cross section of the stele of *Stenomyelon tuedianum* with a double leaf trace at the left. (Drawing based on photograph in Kidston and Gwynne-Vaughan, 1912.) B, diagram of the transverse section of *Calamopitys americana*. (Based on a photograph by Read, 1937.) C, diagrammatic transverse section of the stem of *Diichnia kentuckiensis*. (Redrawn from Read, 1936.) D, *Spermopteris coriacea*, fragment of leaf with abaxial ovules. (Redrawn from Cridland and Morris, 1960.)

The phylogenetic significance and evolutionary position of the Calamopityaceae are still quite uncertain. A number of these forms have been found in the New Albany shale, also the source of many specimens of *Callixylon* (the trunk of *Archaeopteris*), a genus at first considered to be a gymnosperm, but now actually proved to be a fern. Perhaps some of the other genera could also have been cryptogamous rather than seed plants. The primary xylem structure and position of *Diichnia* in many ways resemble those of *Callixylon*.

Other pteridosperms

An interesting seed fern genus from the Carboniferous, not assignable to any of the families mentioned, is based on compression specimens of fertile leaves. *Spermopteris* leaves are long, of the *Taeniopteris* type (see the section on cycadophyte foliage, p. 138), with a single midvein and closely spaced laterals departing at a wide angle. On the abaxial face, on either side of the midvein, is a row of flattened seeds with the micropyles exposed along the edge and directed away from the midvein (Fig. 9-6D).

Mesozoic seed ferns

Some of the Mesozoic seed ferns are extremely interesting and offer intriguing evolutionary possibilities. A brief summary of some of these types will be presented, with notes concerning the possible significance of these plants with respect to the condition of angiospermy.

One of the families of Mesozoic pteridosperms, the Peltaspermaceae, is known from the Upper Triassic of South Africa and Greenland. Leaves, microsporangia, and seed-bearing structures assignable to this family are known. Leaves, called *Lepidopteris,* are pinnately divided, about 30 cm long, and typically fernlike. Pollen-bearing organs are borne on branched structures, smaller than the leaves, and are little elongated sacs, 2 by 1 mm, borne in two rows on the lower sides of some of the ultimate branches (Fig. 9-7). The seeds are of greatest interest; they were borne on the underside of a peltate, stalked structure (Fig. 9-8E). These stalked structures apparently were arranged spirally around a larger axis. This seed-bearing organ has been called a "cupulate disc," and as many as 20 ovules were borne on the underside of the disc.

In some respects, the Corystospermaceae, another family of pteridosperms, represents an advancement over the Peltaspermaceae. Both pollen-bearing organs and seeds are known in this group of plants from the Triassic of South Africa. *Pteruchus* is a small branching system with flattened terminal segments on the lower sides of which were borne elongated sporangia with winged pollen (Fig. 9-8F). This structure is reminiscent of *Crossotheca,* a Paleozoic pteridosperm microsporangiate structure.

Fig. 9-7. Transfer of microsporangiate organs of *Lepidopteris ottonis*. (From Harris, 1932a.)

Among the corystospermaceous seed-bearing genera is *Umkomasia*, also a branched structure, with lateral branches borne in bract axils. Each of these lateral members bore several helmet-shaped (hence the name "Corystospermaceae," which literally means "helmet seed") cupules, each with a single seed within (Fig. 9-8G, H). A similar genus, *Pilophorosperma*, has hairs lining the cupule and the seed is bent at the tip, with the micropyle projecting out at right angles (Fig. 9-8I, J). The cupule of the corystosperms might be regarded as having been derived from a peltate structure, such as that in the Peltaspermaceae, that became more cuplike; or conceivably, seed-bearing structures in both families might represent

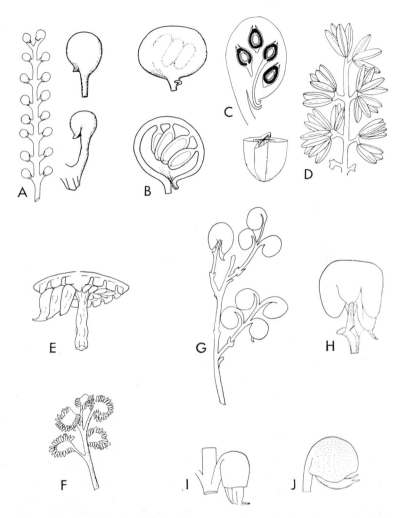

Fig. 9-8. A, *Caytonia Nathorsti*, young megasporophyll and two fruitlike cupulate structures. B, *Caytonia Sewardi*, external view of cupule and sectioned cupule showing ovules. (A and B redrawn from Thomas, 1925.) C, longitudinal section of cupule of *Caytonia Thomasi*. (Redrawn from Harris, 1933.) D, *Caytonanthus Arberi*, portion of microsporophyll and part of a single microsporangium showing the four lobes. (Redrawn from Thomas, 1925.) E, Restoration of part of a cupulate disc of *Lepidopteris ottonis*. (Redrawn from Harris, 1932a.) F, *Pteruchus africanus*, portion of microsporophyll. G, portion of the cupule-bearing axis of *Umkomasia Macleani*. H, one cupule of *U. Macleani* containing a single seed with projecting micropyle. I, cupule of *Pilophorosperma* sp. J, *Pilophorosperma granulatum*, cupule. (F–J redrawn from Thomas, 1933.)

125

specialization of cupulate structures so common among the Paleo-zoic pteridosperms.

The report of a group of Jurassic seed plants, the Caytoniaceae (sometimes included in the order Caytoniales), in 1925 caused a mild botanical sensation. The initial interest in the group was due to its apparent similarity in certain respects to angiosperms. Leaves of the Caytoniaceae are palmately compound, each leaflet having a single main vein with a network of lateral veins. These leaves are included in the genus *Sagenopteris*. The pollen-bearing organ, *Caytonanthus*, consists of a main axis with short lateral branches that may branch again. Suspended from the tips of these ultimate members are elongated, antherlike structures, each with four elongated cavities (Fig. 9-8D). Like *Pteruchus* of the Corystospermaceae, *Caytonanthus* had winged pollen.

The seed-bearing structure, *Caytonia*, consists of a main axis with two rows of saclike structures (Fig. 9-8A). These sacs are recurved, with a liplike projection adjacent to the point of attachment. Within the sac-shaped bodies are small seeds (Fig. 9-8B, C). The earliest work on the group seemed to suggest that the organs in which the seeds are contained were fruits, or carpels, and that the lip might have functioned as a stigma on which pollen grains landed and germinated. In fact, many botany texts published soon after 1925 included the Caytoniaceae in the angiosperms. Subsequent work, however, revealed that pollen grains are actually found *within* the carpellike structures and that these grains must have landed directly on the ovule micropyles. It became obvious, then, that this group was not angiospermous, but represented an assemblage of highly specialized gymnospermous plants with characters allying them with the pteridosperms. The "carpel" is the homologue of the cupule of the Paleozoic pteridosperms and of the seed-bearing discs or cupules of the Mesozoic Peltaspermaceae and Corystospermaceae.

In spite of the fact that the Caytoniaceae cannot be regarded as Mesozoic angiosperms, the group still retains considerable significance as a possible key as to how the angiospermous condition may have evolved. The fruitlike structure in *Caytonia* may be open, but it may represent a stage in a line of evolution directed toward a closed carpel. Furthermore, there are certain angiosperms in which pollen grains occasionally enter the carpel and germinate within the ovary, which is presumably what happened in *Caytonia*.

Much interest is centered on the pteridosperms by some paleobotanists who regard them as possible angiosperm precursors. Certainly, the evolutionary implications of the cupulate structures are interesting, and the Caytoniaceae have achieved a condition that closely approximates the carpel.

Morphologists working with modern plants, however, interpret the carpel as something other than a cupulate structure. They believe that a carpel evolved from a leaf that had laminar ovules, with the leaf having folded to enclose the ovules. Evidence for this idea is well documented by primitive carpels in living plants. On the other hand, there is always the risk that one's thinking may be excessively influenced by what he is expected to find in the fossil record to confirm ideas based on extant plants. Perhaps it would be a more logical step to interpret fossils objectively, allowing for the possibility that structures found among them may alter thinking in connection with modern plant interpretation.

Although the pteridosperms have many aspects that could justify their being considered angiosperm precursors, there are certain difficulties involved as well. For example, typical pteridosperm vascular pitting is circular bordered, with close spacing of the pits. Presumed primitive angiosperms have scalariform pitting, and vessels are supposed to have arisen from scalariform bordered pitted tracheids. Another feature of the seed ferns that cannot readily be interpreted as ancestral to the angiospermous condition is the microsporangiate organ. Many Paleozoic pteridosperms had massive synangiate pollen-bearing structures; others had smaller and less complicated sporangia. If these structures were precursors of angiosperm stamens, however, it would be necessary to regard the entire pteridosperm frond as the homologue of a stamen. Although such a modification of the seed fern leaf is not inconceivable, there are no convincing intermediate stages.

In summary, the Pteridospermales are an important group of extinct plants reflecting a great variety of evolutionary specializations. The closest group of extant plants are the Cycadales, which have large compound frondlike leaves, a similar seed structure, and certain anatomical similarities. It is not improbable that the cycads had their origin among the seed ferns.

With regard to the origin of the pteridosperms themselves, it is no longer a simple matter of regarding them as intermediate between the ferns and the rest of the gymnosperms. There is no substantial evidence to indicate that the pteridosperms originated from true ferns. True, the ancestral types may have had many fernlike characters, and certain features of the Pteridospermales are quite like those in ferns. On the other hand, it is probable that these similarities reflect parallel developments, or even origins of the ferns and seed ferns from a group of plants not exactly in either category. Certain forms, such as *Tetraxylopteris,* some of the Cladoxylales, and others that may have been important primitive types, have already been discussed.

CYCADEOIDALES

The extinct order Cycadeoidales (frequently called Bennett-itales, especially among European workers) was an important Meso-zoic group that contributed to the usual referral of the Mesozoic era as the "Age of Cycads." Although in many ways distinct from the order Cycadales, the Cycadeoidales have certain features in common with the cycads, many of which are still living. Two important families are included in the Cycadeoidales: the Williamsoniaceae and the Cycadeoidaceae. In general, the Williamsoniaceae have more or less elongated stems that branched more profusely than did those of the Cycadeoidaceae. *Williamsonia gigas* is generally represented as an unbranched, erect plant, about two meters tall, with a stem covered with rhombic leaf scars. At the apex was a crown of pinnately compound leaves (*Zamites*), and among the leaf bases were produced the fruiting structures, or cones. Cones were borne on bract-covered peduncles, and an unopened cone bud somewhat resembled an artichoke bud. The structure of the cone is still imperfectly known, but it appears that within the enveloping bracts there is a conical receptacle covered with stalked ovules packed among sterile, fleshy scales (interseminal scales). Other specimens referable to *W. gigas* have been found that appear to be the pollen-bearing organs. These structures have a basal, urn-shaped portion at the upper edges of which were free microsporophylls. It is still not known whether the pollen-bearing cones were borne separately from the seed cones, or whether the micro-sporophylls were attached to the distal end of the ovulate receptacle.

Williamsonia Sewardiana is an upright, branched species from the Jurassic of India (Fig. 9-9A). It, too, has a trunk covered with flattened, rhombic leaf bases and a terminal crown of compound leaves (*Ptilophyllum*). It differs from *W. gigas* in that instead of occurring among leaf bases, cones terminate short branches. Only ovu-

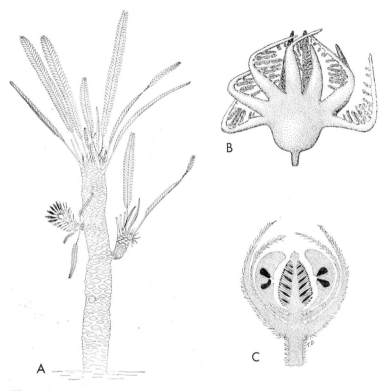

Fig. 9-9. A, reconstruction of *Williamsonia Sewardiana*. (Redrawn from Sahni, 1932.) B, microsporangiate cone of *Williamsonia spectabilis*. (Redrawn from Thomas, 1913.) C, diagrammatic longitudinal section of the cone of *Williamsoniella coronata*. (Redrawn from Harris, 1944.)

late cones are known, and as in *W. gigas* the scale-covered peduncle is terminated by a cone-shaped ovulate receptacle on which are stalked ovules and many interseminal scales.

Other cones of *Williamsonia* are known that appear to be only microsporangiate. In *W. spectabilis*, for example, the microsporangiate fructification is cup-shaped at the base, with its upper margin divided into a number of free, outspreading appendages that are incurved at the tips (Fig. 9-9B). The free appendages are pinnately divided, with pollen sacs borne along the pinnae. These sporangia are not simple but are divided into a number of cavities within. Other species represent modifications of this same theme. *Williamsonia mexicana*, from the Triassic of Oaxaca, Mexico, has a deep urn-shaped portion with many short, slender, free marginal appendages. *Williamsonia whitbiensis* has synangia borne on the inner face of the free appendages rather than on lateral pinnae. Other isolated ovulate cones are known that agree in general structure with those of *W. gigas* and *W. Sewardiana*. It is thus apparent that much is left unanswered concerning the structure of williamsonian cones and the question of whether the cones were monosporangiate or bisporangiate. And if these cones are monosporangiate, are both the microsporangiate and ovulate cones borne on the same plant or on separate plants?

Williamsoniella is a related genus known to have bisporangiate cones. This genus is branched and shrubby, with dichotomously branching stem axes and entire leaves (*Nilssoniopteris*). The leaves, a little over a decimeter in length, are oblong, lanceolate, with a prominent midrib and closely spaced lateral veins attached almost perpendicularly. Cones were first described as having been borne in the angles of the dichotomies of the stem, but later work suggests a possible axillary position. Terminating a slender peduncle is an ovulate receptacle not unlike those of *Williamsonia;* interseminal scales and ovules with projecting micropyles covered the surface of the slender receptacle. Below the ovule-bearing region is a whorl of a dozen or more microsporophylls shaped roughly like sectors of spheres, with the narrow edges inward, and each borne on a short stalk (Fig. 9-9C). On the ventral face of each sporophyll are several projections bearing pollen capsules. Four such capsules is the usual number, and each capsule contains several spore masses. Below the microsporophylls is a set of perianth-like, hairy, slender bracts.

The Upper Triassic *Wielandiella,* from Sweden, is another member of the Williamsoniaceae and had a branching habit similar to that of *Williamsoniella.* Actually, the branching was not really a dichotomous type because apical growth appeared to have been terminated by a cone, beneath which two lateral branches arose. Leaves of the genus *Anomozamites* were probably borne on the stems. These leaves are about eight cm long, lanceolate, with the lamina divided deeply into truncate segments, and were clustered near the regions of branching. The poorly preserved reproductive structures have an ovulate receptacle like those typical of the Williamsoniaceae — a central column on which were borne ovules and interseminal scales.

In contrast with the Williamsoniaceae, members of the Cycadeoidaceae (Bennettitaceae) generally had squat, unbranched, or sparsely branched trunks. Silicified trunks of the genus *Cycadeoidea* (*Bennettites*) occur in rocks of late Jurassic and Cretaceous age and have wide geographical distribution. The unbranched trunks are spherical, ellipsoidal or ovoid, or sometimes conical, and resemble to some extent an old-fashioned straw beehive. Indeed, some of the early amateur collectors believed that these interesting specimens actually were fossilized beehives. In some instances, two or more of these trunks were attached, representing branching specimens. Covering the surface of these stems is an armor of bases of leaves packed among a dense ramentum composed of long, flat, multicellular hairlike structures. These persistent leaf bases are reminiscent of certain modern cycads or of certain palm trees that retain the bases of leaves after leaves die. Although no leaves have been found attached to these stems, it is assumed that the tip of the trunk bore a crown of large pinnately compound leaves. In some well-preserved specimens, young, undeveloped, folded leaves are found at the extreme tips, and these definitely show a pinnate construction.

A trunk of *Cycadeoidea* has a large stele, most of which is pith. Around the pith is a cylinder of xylem composed of scalariform and circular bordered pitted tracheids and many large rays. Phloem is often preserved and is sometimes quite thick. In the wide cortex are many leaf traces, ideally C-shaped in cross section, and outside of the stem proper is the dense armor.

Cones of *Cycadeoidea* were borne among the persistent leaf bases, and their structure, worked out by G. R. Wieland, has been reproduced by many workers. His reconstruction shows a long peduncle, covered with long, simple, ramentum-covered bracts in helical arrangement. At the tip of the peduncle, which may be several centimeters long, is a conical ovulate receptacle, covered with the familiar ovules and interseminal scales. In young cones the ovules were apparently sessile. At the base of the ovulate receptacle was supposed to have been a fused whorl of expanded micro-sporophylls, up to about 20 in number. Each sporophyll was pictured as a pinnately compound structure, with two rows of pollen sacs borne on each lateral pinna. Pollen sacs were actually compound structures, with 20 to 30 individual sporangia within.

No such opened cones have ever been seen, and Wieland's conclusions were based on what appeared to have been immature cones with the microsporophylls tightly curled against the ovulate receptacle. His reconstruction was based on the way he believed such a cone would look when fully expanded.

More recent work on these cones, however, has demonstrated that there were no individual microsporophylls, but that the pollen-producing region was a massive compound synangium with a fleshy, distal, dome-shaped sterile mass of tissue (Fig. 9-10A). What appeared to have been pinnae of infolded sporophylls are actually trabeculae within the massive synangium on which the pollen sacs were produced. In view of the typical pollen-bearing organs in the Williamsoniaceae, the cones of which in many ways approximate those of the Cycadeoidaceae, it may be possible to conclude that the cycadeoid synangium originated through a fusion of individual microsporophylls.

In *Cycadeoidea* the pollen-bearing organs are believed to have been shed after pollination, and as the ovule matured, they became elevated on long, slender stalks. The interseminal scales also elongated, and the micropyles of the ovules projected beyond the club-shaped tips of the sterile scales. Embryos are occasionally preserved in mature cycadeoidean seeds, and it is possible to see that they are dicotyledonous.

Monanthesia is the generic name assigned to petrified cyca-deoid trunks that have a cone in every leaf axil. In other respects, including vegetative anatomy and cone structure, it differs little from *Cycadeoidea*. As fas as is known, however, *Monanthesia* is more typically late Cretaceous in age.

In general structure a cycadeoid plant resembles closely one of the squat members of the contemporary Cycadales. It is obvious, however, that vegetative anatomy and cone structure are quite different.

The complexity of the cone in the Cycadeoidaceae and, in-

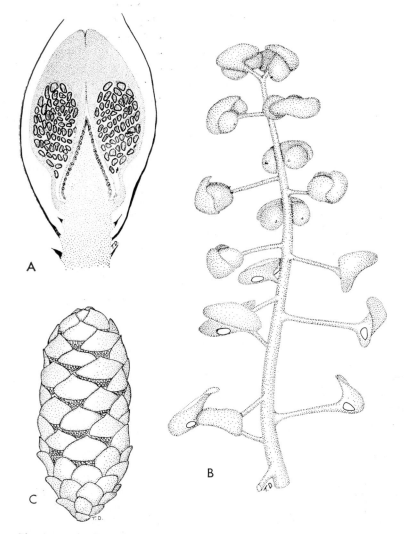

Fig. 9-10. A, diagrammatic longitudinal section of a cone of *Cycadeoidea* sp. (From Delevoryas, 1963.) B, *Beania gracilis*, axis bearing megasporophylls. C, *Androstrobus manis*, microsporangiate cone. (B and C redrawn from Harris, 1941.)

deed, in all of the Cycadeoidales, leads one to wonder about its morphological nature. At first glance it might appear to be a modified stem covered with spirally arranged leaves (hairy bracts), followed by a whorl of microspore-bearing foliar appendages, and terminated in a receptacle on which are borne the ovules. If it were a branch, however, one would expect to find the origin of the cone vascular system from the stem stele, just above the level of separation of a leaf trace. Indeed, that is the way traces to vegetative lateral branches arise. Cone vascular supplies, however, do not originate from the stele of the stem. The source of the peduncle stele is branches of two or more leaf traces, none of which, in some species, happens to be the trace of the leaf that subtends the cone. The origin of a cone from foliar vascular bundles makes it tempting to believe that cycadeoid cones are parts of a leaf system. The fact that cones may lie in axils of leaves whose traces contributed nothing to the formation of the cone stele might be explained on the basis of the foreshortening of the stem of *Cycadeoidea* from a once more-elongated ancestral type. How to explain the origin of the cone stele from more than one leaf trace is another problem. Perhaps this also has something to do with the telescoping of the stem.

CYCADALES

The true cycads, of the order Cycadales, were in existence since early Triassic times, or, perhaps, even earlier. There is good evidence that the order originated from the pteridosperm complex. Leaves are leathery and compound, seeds are borne on modified foliar structures, and the seed anatomy is quite similar to that of the pteridosperms. The origin of a megasporophyll of the Cycadales from a large, seed-bearing frond is well documented even among the living cycads. *Cycas revoluta* has no distinct cone and the megasporophylls are loosely arranged in a fertile zone at the tip of the plant. Each sporophyll is quite leaflike, with distal pinnate segments. Proximally, ovules are borne along either side of the rachis. Such a megasporophyll represents a reduction from a seed-fern type of fertile leaf that was pinnately divided, with ovules taking the place of pinnules. In *Cycas media* the terminal portion of the leaf is not as well developed as in *C. revoluta*, with pinnae reduced to mere serrations. *Dioon* has a still more reduced sporophyll, with a terminal lamina and two proximal ovules directed toward the stem axis. Furthermore, a definite cone, with compactly arranged megasporophylls, is present in *Dioon*. *Macrozamia* has a still smaller sporophyll, with the distal portion represented by a spine. Finally, in *Zamia*, a peltate structure with two inwardly directed ovules is all that remains of the megasporophyll. Among the fossil cycads, megasporophyll modifications corresponding to those among modern cycads can be found.

An early Mesozoic cycad that has been reconstructed is the Upper Triassic *Bjuvia simplex*, an erect, unbranched tree about three meters tall. Persistent leaf bases clothed the trunk, which bore a terminal crown of leaves (*Taeniopteris*) that were large and entire, and shaped something like banana leaves. As in *Cycas*, the megasporophylls (*Palaeocycas*) are arranged in a loose terminal cluster. Ovules are borne along the rachis, which has an expanded distal portion, not too unlike the situation in a *Cycas* megasporophyll. Association of all of these parts was based on a study of epidermal features evident on cuticular remains. The pollen-bearing organ is unknown.

The Jurassic deposits at Yorkshire, which yielded remains of the famous Caytoniaceae, are also the source of interesting cycadalean material. *Beania* is a loose megasporangiate strobilus with stalked megasporophylls borne at right angles to the cone axis (Fig. 9-10B). Projecting inward from the peltate head are two ovules, and each sporophyll closely resembles a *Zamia* megasporophyll. *Zamia* cones, of course, are much more compact than are those in *Beania*.

Androstrobus manis is a pollen-bearing cone found in the same beds, and on the basis of epidermal structure, it is assumed to be the microsporangiate cone of the same kind of plant that bore the seed-bearing *Beania* (Fig. 9-10C). *Androstrobus* is like a modern cycad pollen-bearing cone; it is a few centimeters long, having helically arranged microsporophylls with sporangia on the abaxial surface. Leaves of the genus *Nilssonia* (to be discussed) are also found in these Yorkshire deposits and are thought to be part of the same plant that carried *Beania* and *Androstrobus*.

Cycadophyte foliage

Cycadophyte foliage, abundant in Mesozoic strata, has been studied extensively through analyses of cuticular remains. On the basis of epidermal characters it is possible to distinguish two main groups of cycadophyte leaves. Two orders are recognized: the Bennettitales and the Nilssoniales (these seem to correspond pretty closely to the Cycadeoidales and the Cycadales, respectively). One of the important epidermal characters utilized in this separation is the structure of stomatal apparatuses. In one type of stomatal ontogeny, a single mother cell divides to produce two guard cells; certain of the adjacent epidermal cells become modified into subsidiary cells. This type of stoma is referred to as *haplocheilic* and is typical of the fossil Nilssoniales. A more complex stomatal apparatus develops, however, when a single mother cell divides twice to produce three cells, with the middle cell dividing again to form two guard cells. In other words, the subsidiary cells and guard cells come from the same initial. Such a stomatal apparatus is called *syndetocheilic* and it is found among the Bennettitales. The stomatal types described are fairly constant and seem to be distinguishable among widely separated groups of plants. For example, the haplocheilic type is found not only in the fossil Nilssoniales, but in the Cycadales, Pteridospermales, fossil and living conifers (including the Cordaitales), Ginkgoales, and in *Ephedra*. Syndetocheilic stomata are found in the Bennettitales (leaf order), Cycadeoidales, and in *Gnetum* and *Welwitschia*. Angiosperms have both types of stomatal apparatuses.

In addition to syndetocheilic stomata, leaves of the Bennettitales show heavy cutinization of the guard cells, especially on the outer wall and on the walls adjacent to the subsidiary cells. Among the Bennettitales the ordinary epidermal cells are frequently arranged in rows, and their walls are wavy. Stomata are usually oriented with their long axes perpendicular to the veins. Judging from epidermal characters of certain parts of the Cycadeoidales, it is probable that leaves of the Bennettitales belong to members of the Cycadeoidales.

Leaves of the Nilssoniales probably represent the foliage of fossil members of the Cycadales. There is less cuticular thickening on nilssonialean guard cells than on those of the Bennettitales. Epidermal cells have straight walls and are not arranged in regular rows. Furthermore, the orientation of the stomata is not regular.

Following are very brief descriptions of some of the Mesozoic cycadophyte leaf genera, introduced only to clarify earlier refer-

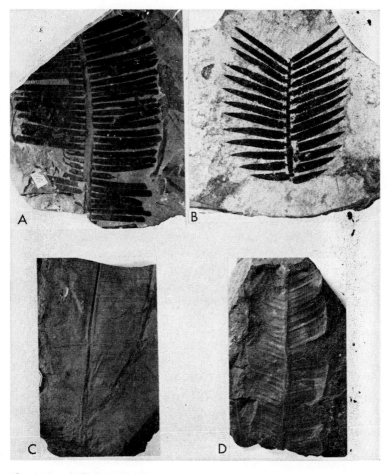

Fig. 9-11. A, leaf of *Pterophyllum*. B, *Zamites*. C, portion of a leaf of *Macrotaeniopteris*. D, *Nilssonia*.

ences made to leaf types in association with other parts of the plants.

Bennettitales: Pterophyllum is a common leaf genus having long, slender pinnae, with parallel margins, attached to the rachis broadly at the base; the angle of divergence approaches a right angle (Fig. 9-11A). *Anomozamites* is similar and sometimes is included within the genus *Pterophyllum*. In *Anomozamites* the segments of the lamina may be unequal, are shorter, broader, and truncate. In *Ptilophyllum* pinnae are linear or lanceolate, attached obliquely to the rachis, and overlap at their bases, which are rounded. *Zamites* (Fig. 9-11B) is very similar to *Ptilophyllum;* pinnae are attached obliquely or, sometimes, at right angles to the upper surface of the rachis, although not covering it as in *Ptilophyllum.* The pinnae are generally contracted near their bases. Pinnae of *Otozamites* have constricted bases and are attached to the upper surface of the frond rachis. They are broadly oval or sometimes almost orbicular, and the anterior pinna lobe is more pronounced than the posterior one. *Dictyozamites* also has constricted pinna bases attached to the rachis in the middle. Bases overlap and cover the upper surface of the rachis; veins form an anastomosing network. In *Pseudocycas,* pinnae are linear and attached broadly at the base, with a sometimes decurrent posterior margin. Only a midrib is present in each pinna. *Taeniopteris* is the name given to an entire leaf that has a prominent midrib with lateral veins that depart at right angles, or at a slightly ascending angle, to the midrib. The name *Taeniopteris* is used when no epidermal features are present; when bennettitalean cuticle is preserved, these leaves are then called *Nilssoniopteris.*

Nilssoniales: Nilssonia is a common form that may have a large, entire frond, but, more typically, the lamina is cut into segments of various sizes and shapes, even in the same leaf (Fig. 9-11D). The lamina is attached to the upper surface of the rachis and covers it. Veins depart from the midvein at right angles or ascend slightly. *Ctenis* includes cycadean leaves, some of which may attain a length of two meters. The pinnae are long and ascending, and several parallel veins enter each leaflet; occasionally these are connected by small cross veins. *Pseudoctenis* is similar but lacks connecting veins. *Doratophyllum* is the nilssonialean counterpart of the bennettitalean genus of *Taeniopteris*-like foliage, *Nilssoniopteris.* *Macrotaeniopteris* is like *Doratophyllum* but much larger, sometimes attaining a length of a meter (Fig. 9-11C). It is often included within *Taeniopteris.*

Other cycadophyte leaves are known from the Mesozoic, but because of the absence of cuticles they cannot be assigned to either the Bennettitales or the Nilssoniales.

In summarizing the cycadophytes, one might attempt to determine evolutionary trends in the class. That the pteridosperms probably gave rise to the two other orders, Cycadeoidales and Cycadales, is probable. Such an evolutionary development to the Cycadales is much more simple to understand than is the origin of a group such as the Cycadeoidales. In the Cycadales, it is obvious that there has been a reduction in the size of the leaf-bearing, fertile structures from a large, two or more times compound, leaf to the small peltate megasporophyll in the seed cone of *Zamia* and to the small flattened microsporophyll in the same genus. Vegetative fronds have been slightly altered, but the same type of stomatal apparatus is found both in the seed ferns and in the Cycadales. The Cycadeoidales may have separated from the seed ferns at a much earlier time. Even in the early Mesozoic, and perhaps before, the cycadeoids were distinct from the true cycads.

REFERENCES

ANDREWS, H. N., 1940. "On the stelar anatomy of the pteridosperms with particular reference to the secondary wood," *Ann. Missouri Botan. Gard.*, 27: 51–118.

———, 1945. "Contributions to our knowledge of American Carboniferous floras VII. Some pteridosperm stems from Iowa," *Ann. Missouri Botan. Gard.*, 32: 323–360.

———, 1948. "Some evolutionary trends in the pteridosperms," *Botan. Gaz.*, 110: 13–31.

ARNOLD, C. A., 1948. "Classification of gymnosperms from the viewpoint of paleobotany," *Botan. Gaz.*, 110: 1–12.

———, 1952. "Observations on fossil plants from the Devonian of eastern North America VI. *Xenocladia medullosina* Arnold," *Univ. Michigan Contr. Mus. Paleont.*, 9: 297–309.

———, 1953. "Origin and relationships of the cycads," *Phytomorphology*, 3: 51–65.

BAXTER, R. W., 1949. "Some pteridosperm stems and fructifications with particular reference to the medullosae," *Ann. Missouri Botan. Gard.*, 36: 287–352.

BENSON, MARGARET, 1914. "*Sphaerostoma ovale* (*Conostoma ovale* et *intermedianum*, Williamson), a Lower Carboniferous ovule from Pettycur, Fifeshire, Scotland," *Trans. Roy. Soc. Edinburgh*, 50: 1–15.

CRIDLAND, A. A., and J. E. MORRIS, 1960. "*Spermopteris*, a new genus of pteridosperms from the Upper Pennsylvanian of Kansas," *Amer. Jour. Botan.*, 47: 855–859.

DELEVORYAS, T., 1955. "The medullosae — structure and relationships," *Palaeontographica*, 97B: 114–167.

Delevoryas, T., 1959. "Investigations of North American cycadeoids: *Monanth:sia*," *Amer. Jour. Botan.*, **46**: 657–666.

———, 1961. "Notes on the cone of *Cycadeoidea*," *Amer. Jour. Botan.*, **48**: 540 (abstract).

———, 1963. "Investigations of North American cycadeoids: cones of *Cycadeoidea*," *Amer. J. Botan.* (in press).

———, and Jeanne Morgan, 1954. "A new pteridosperm from Upper Pennsylvanian deposits of North America," *Palaeontographica*, **96B**: 12–23.

Florin, R., 1933. "Studien über die Cycadales des Mesozoikums nebst Erörtungen über die Spaltöffnungsapparate der Bennettitales," *Kungl. Svenska Vetenskapsakad. Handl.*, 3rd ser. **12** (5): 1–134.

Gordon, W. T., 1938. "On *Tetrastichia bupatides*: a Carboniferous pteridosperm from East Lothian," *Trans. Roy. Soc. Edinburgh*, **59**: 351–370.

Hall, J. W., 1952. "The phloem of *Heterangium americanum*," *Amer. Midl. Nat.*, **47**: 763–768.

———, 1954. "The genus *Stephanospermum* in American coal balls," *Botan. Gaz.*, **115**: 346–360.

Halle, T. G., 1933. "The structure of certain fossil spore-bearing organs believed to belong to pteridosperms," *Kungl. Svenska Vetenskapsakad. Handl.*, 3rd ser., **12** (6): 1–103.

Harris, T. M., 1932a. "The fossil flora of Scoresby Sound East Greenland. Part 2: Description of seed plants *incertae sedis* together with a discussion of certain cycadophyte cuticles," *Medd. Grønland*, **85** (3): 1–112.

———, 1932b. "The fossil flora of Scoresby Sound East Greenland. Part 3: Caytoniales and Bennettitales," *Medd. Grønland*, **85** (5): 1–133.

———, 1933. "A new member of the Caytoniales," *New Phytol.*, **32**: 97–114.

———, 1940. "On *Caytonia* Thomas," *Ann. Botan.*, n.s., **4**: 713–734.

———, 1941a. "*Caytonanthus*, the microsporophyll of *Caytonia*," *Ann. Botan.*, n.s., **5**: 47–58.

———, 1941b. "Cones of extinct Cycadales from the Jurassic of Yorkshire," *Phil. Trans. Roy. Soc. London*, **231B**: 75–98.

———, 1944. "A revision of *Williamsoniella*," *Phil. Trans. Roy. Soc. London*, **231B**: 313–328.

Hirmer, M., 1933. "Zur Kenntnis der strukturbietenden Pflanzenreste des jungeren Palaeozoikums," *Palaeontographica*, **78B**: 57–113.

Hoskins, J. H., and A. T. Cross, 1946. "Studies in the Trigonocarpales. Part II. Taxonomic problems and a revision of the genus *Pachytesta*," *Amer. Midl. Nat.*, **36**: 331–361.

Jongmans, W. J., 1954. "Contributions to the knowledge of the flora of the seam Girondelle (lower part of the Westphalian A) Part I," *Geol. Sticht. C*, III, 1: no. 4.

Kidston, R., and D. T. Gwynne-Vaughan, 1912. "On the Carboniferous flora of Berwickshire. Part I.— *Stenomyelon tuedianum* Kidston," *Trans. Roy. Soc. Edinburgh*, **48**: 263–271.

Nathorst, A. G., 1909. "Paläobotanischen Mitteilungen. No. 8," *Kungl. Svenska Vetenskapsakad. Handl.*, **45** (4): 1–33.

NEELEY, FLORENCE E., 1951. "Small petrified seeds from the Pennsylvanian of Illinois," *Botan. Gaz.*, **113**: 165–179.

OLIVER, F. W., 1904. "On the structure and affinities of *Stephanospermum*, Brongniart, a genus of fossil gymnosperm seeds," *Trans. Linn. Soc. London (Botany)*, **6**: 361–400.

———, 1909. "On *Physostoma elegans*, Williamson, an archaic type of seed from the Palaeozoic rocks," *Ann. Botan.*, **23**: 73–116.

———, and E. J. SALISBURY, 1911. "On the structure and affinities of the Palaeozoic seeds of the *Conostoma* group," *Ann. Botan.*, **25**: 1–50.

———, and D. H. SCOTT, 1904. "On the structure of the Palaeozoic seed *Lagenostoma Lomaxi*, with a statement of the evidence upon which it is referred to *Lyginodendron*," *Phil. Trans. Roy. Soc. London*, **197B**: 193–247.

READ, C. B., 1936. "The flora of the New Albany shale. Part 1. *Diichnia kentuckiensis*, a new representative of the Calamopityeae," *U.S. Geol. Surv. Prof. Paper*, **185-H**: 149–161.

———, 1937. "The flora of the New Albany shale. Part 2. The Calamopityeae and their relationships," *U.S. Geol. Surv. Prof. Paper*, **186-E**: 81–104.

———, and G. CAMPBELL, 1939. "Preliminary account of the New Albany shale flora," *Amer. Midl. Nat.*, **21**: 435–448.

REMY, W., 1953. "Beiträge zur Kenntnis der Rotliegenflora Thüringens. Teil I. Zwei bisher unbekannte Pteridospermen-Fruktifikationen aus dem Thüringer Rotliegenden," *Sitzungs. deutsch. Akad. Wiss. Berlin (Math.-Naturwiss. Kl.)*, **1953** (1): 1–24.

SAHNI, B., 1932. "A petrified *Williamsonia* (*W. Sewardiana*, sp. nov.) from the Rajmahal Hills, India," *Paleont. Indica*, n.s., **20** (3): 1–19.

SCHOPF, J. M., 1949. "Pteridosperm male fructifications: American species of *Dolerotheca*, with notes regarding certain allied forms," *J. Paleont.*, **22**: 681–724.

SELLARDS, E. H., 1907. "Notes on the spore-bearing organ *Codonotheca* and its relationship with the Cycadofilices," *New Phytol.*, **6**: 175–178.

STEWART, W. N., 1954. "The structure and affinities of *Pachytesta illinoense* comb. nov.," *Amer. J. Botan.*, **41**: 500–508.

———, 1958. "The structure and relationships of *Pachytesta composita* sp. nov.," *Amer. J. Botan.*, **45**: 580–588.

———, and T. DELEVORYAS, 1956. "The medullosan pteridosperms," *Botan. Rev.*, **22**: 45–80.

THOMAS, H. H., 1913. "The fossil flora of the Cleveland district," *Quart. J. Geol. Soc. London*, **69**: 223–251.

———, 1925. "The Caytoniales, a new group of angiospermous plants from the Jurassic rocks of Yorkshire," *Phil. Trans. Roy. Soc. London*, **213B**: 299–363.

———, 1933. "On some pteridospermous plants from the Mesozoic rocks of South Africa," *Phil. Trans. Roy. Soc. London*, **222B**: 193–265.

———, and NELLIE BANCROFT, 1913. "On the cuticles of some recent and fossil cycadean fronds," *Trans. Linn. Soc. London (Botany)*, **8**: 155–204.

TOWNROW, J. A., 1960. "The Peltaspermaceae, a pteridosperm family of Permian and Triassic age," *Palaeontology*, **3**: 333–361.

WEBER, O., and J. T. STERZEL, 1896. "Beiträge zur Kenntnis der Medulloseae," *Naturwiss. Ges. Chemnitz, Ber.*, **13**: 44–143.

WIELAND, G. R., 1906. *American Fossil Cycads*, Washington, D.C.: Carnegie Inst.

———, 1916. *American Fossil Cycads*, Vol. II, *Taxonomy*, Washington, D.C.: Carnegie Inst.

chapter ten ❯ Problematical
Cycadophytes

Certain fossil plant groups seem to have some affinities with the Cycadophyta, but are not close enough to be placed within that class. They will be discussed here because they have some features in common with the cycadophytes, and not with the implication that they actually are members of that group.

One of these fossil plant assemblages is sometimes placed in its own order, the Pentoxylales, and it comes from the Jurassic of India (Fig. 10-1A). The stem, *Pentoxylon,* resembles that of *Medullosa* in certain respects. There are generally five steles, sometimes six, arranged in a cylinder; each small protostele is surrounded by considerable secondary xylem that is thicker toward the center of the stem than toward the outside. Additional smaller steles may alternate with the principal ones. In general structure, the wood is more typically coniferous than cycadophytic; tracheids are narrow, wood is compact, and on the radial walls of the tracheids are crowded circular bordered pits. On these stems are borne short shoots, very much like some of the older dwarf shoots in *Ginkgo.* These short shoots are covered with closely spaced leaf bases, and distally they bore a crown of leaves called *Nipaniophyllum,* which resemble very closely *Taeniopteris*-type foliage. Stomata, however, are of the bennettitalean type.

On some of the short shoots were borne seed-bearing branches. The seed-bearing peduncle divided into several branches, and each

143

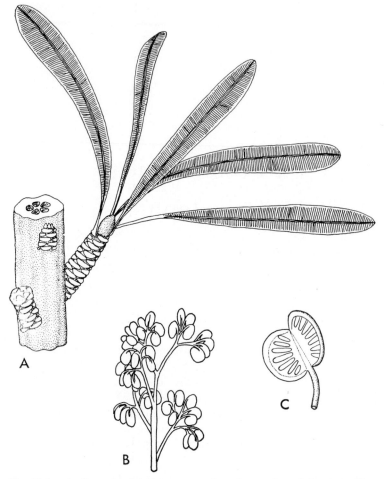

Fig. 10-1. A, *Pentoxylon Sahnii*, reconstruction of a portion of the stem. (Redrawn from Sahni, 1948, by permission of Univ. of Chicago Press.) B, *Harrisiothecium (Hydropteridangium) marsilioides*, portion of microsporophyll. C, single, opened synangium of *H. marsilioides*. (B and C redrawn from Harris, 1932.)

branch was terminated by a cone. The seeds are sessile on the cone axis and have thick, fleshy integuments. No scales, leaves, bracts, or other accompanying structures are found on the cone axes in association with the seeds, which are attached at the base and have outwardly projecting micropyles. *Carnoconites* is the name applied to the seed-bearing branches.

Sahnia is the name given to the probable microsporangiate organs that were borne terminally on shoots and fused basally into a shallow disc or cup. The microsporangiate organs themselves were slender branched axes, with the terminal segments bearing small sporangia. Thus the Pentoxylales seem to represent a group combining characters of various other groups. While stem anatomy is more nearly like that of the conifers than any other group, the polystelic condition resembles certain pteridosperms. Leaves are definitely cycadophytic. Seed-bearing structures are quite distinct, with certain similarities to those of the Ginkgoales. Microsporangiate structures, too, are unlike any others.

Rhexoxylon, a Triassic genus, is known only from stem fragments, one species of which originates in Antarctica. The parenchymatous pith contains secretory cavities, nests of sclereids, and scattered vascular strands. Around the pith is a ring of bundles that appear to be entirely secondary in origin. Each of the bundles has a centripetal portion and a centrifugal part, with parenchyma between. Larger masses of vascular tissue occur outside of this cylinder and are separated by very wide rays. This outer tissue has some primary tracheids on the inner face, but the bulk is secondary. Rays are narrow, wood is compact, and pitting is circular bordered as in many conifers. The position of *Rhexoxylon* is uncertain; in some respects it appears medullosan, but the differences far outweigh the similarities.

Hydropteridangium, a microsporangiate structure from the Upper Triassic of Greenland, consists of a main axis with branches arising from it. These laterals again divide three-dimensionally and end in the spore-containing structures (Fig. 10-1B, C). Each of these spore sacs is flattened-ellipsoidal and consists of two valves connected along one edge. Each valve has embedded in it about seven elongate sporangia; microspores are winged. Cuticles of supposedly related leaves (*Ptilozamites*) have gymnospermous stomata, but not like those of the Bennettitales. If the leaves are actually those of *Hydropteridangium*, the affinities of the latter would appear to be closer to the cycadophytes than to any other group. Recently *Harrisiothecium* was proposed as the more appropriate name for these microsporangiate organs.

Another group of plants, probably gymnospermous, that has been classified at various times with the ferns, seed ferns, cycads, and angiosperms occurs in Permian rocks on various continents in

Fig. 10-2. *Scutum Leslium* associated with *Glossopteris Browniana.* (From Plumstead, 1956.)

the southern hemisphere. Many of the leaves of this group of plants are called *Glossopteris* and, as the name suggests, are tongue-shaped or spatulate, or sometimes more elongated (Fig. 10-2). The length ranges from a few centimeters to a few decimeters. Each leaf has a prominent midvein from which arise lateral, anastomosing smaller veins. From the adaxial face of the leaf, or, in some species, from the upper surface of the petiole, arises the reproductive organ, which has been variously interpreted. The stalked, reproductive structure, placed in the genus *Scutum*, appears to have been constructed of two concave valves, with the concavities facing each other. A winglike margin lines the edge of each valve. Small saclike structures occur in the concavity of the adaxial valve. The exact nature of these bodies is unknown, but one interpretation that must be open to question is that they represent carpels. On the abaxial half, in the concavity, are structures that one author believes to be the pollen sacs. A precise interpretation is not yet possible because most of the fossil fertile material is in the form of impressions that cannot be examined with any degree of accuracy. There is perhaps no justification for discussing these plants with the cycadophytes rather than with any other group of plants, but even though the exact nature of the reproductive structures has not yet been worked out, it seems likely that these plants were seed plants, and the fernlike leaf suggests a possible relationship with the seed ferns. It seems definite, also, that the reproductive structures were borne on leaves, another cycadophyte character.

Gangamopteris is another leaf genus similar to *Glossopteris* but differing primarily in the absence of a midrib.

Poorly preserved axes, which may have been stems or roots, and placed in the genus *Vertebraria*, have sometimes been thought to belong to *Glossopteris* leaves. Evidence for this, however, is not at all certain. *Vertebraria* has a most unusual stele; the vascular skeleton appears to have been constructed of several plates of vascular tissue radiating from a common center. Very broad parenchymatous rays separate these arms of xylem. Horizontal plates of vascular tissue connect adjacent plates of xylem and phloem at various intervals. Pitting is gymnospermous, with two or three rows of generally opposite pits.

The significance of these unusual and apparently unique gymnospermous plants is not yet fully understood. Perhaps they are merely isolated examples of several extinct groups of gymnospermous plants, not quite identical with the presently known taxa. Combined within some of these forms are characters found in the ferns, seed ferns, cycadophytes, ginkgophytes, and other conifers.

REFERENCES

HARRIS, T. M., 1932. "The fossil flora of Scoresby Sound East Greenland. Part 3: Caytoniales and Bennettitales," *Medd. Grønland,* **85** (5): 1–133.

LUNDBLAD, BRITTA, 1961. "*Harrisiothecium* nomen novum," *Taxon,* **10:** 23–24.

PLUMSTEAD, EDNA P., 1952. "Description of two new genera and six new species of fructifications borne on *Glossopteris* leaves," *Trans. Geol. Soc. South Africa,* **55:** 281–328.

———, 1956. "Bisexual fructifications on *Glossopteris* leaves from South Africa," *Palaeontographica,* **100B:** 1–25.

SAHNI, B., 1948. "The Pentoxyleae: a new group of Jurassic gymnosperms from the Rajmahal Hills of India," *Botan. Gaz.,* **110:** 47–80.

VISHNU-MITTRE, 1953. "A male flower of the Pentoxyleae with remarks on the structure of the female cones of the group," *Palaeobotanist,* **2:** 75–84.

WALTON, J., 1923. "On *Rhexoxylon*, Bancroft — a Triassic genus of plants exhibiting a liane-type of vascular organization," *Phil. Trans. Roy. Soc. London*, **212B:** 79–109.

――――, 1956. "*Rhexoxylon* and *Dadoxylon* from the Lower Shire region of Nyasaland and Portuguese East Africa," *Colonial Geol. and Mineral Resources* (London), **6:** 159–168.

chapter eleven

Subdivision Pteropsida Class Coniferophyta

Until Devonian seeds are found, the occurrence of coniferophytes in that period cannot be assumed with certainty. A number of Devonian plant fossils with coniferous vegetative structure are known, but such was the case with *Callixylon*, which turned out to be an arborescent fern trunk. Nevertheless, this class has had a long history and is still flourishing.

In contrast with the cycadophytes, the Coniferophyta have simple leaves that may be linear, awl-shaped, fan-shaped, divided, or of a variety of other shapes, and that are most often sessile. Leaf traces are small and usually single or double. Secondary vascular tissues are abundant, with narrow, compactly arranged tracheids, and with small rays and generally little parenchyma in the xylem. Fructifications are borne on modified branch systems.

The origin of the coniferophyte line remains a puzzle. It would be tempting to regard the pteridosperms as possible conifer precursors, but with continuing paleobotanical investigations such an idea becomes more difficult to prove. The coniferophytes existed as an independent line as long as did the seed ferns, and deriving one group from the other does not seem to fit the facts. Thus one is left to speculate as to what the ancestors of the coniferophytes

149

might have been. Perhaps one or more groups of Devonian fern-like plants, which had retained certain psilophytic characters, are a logical source. This is not to imply that conifers came from ferns, but, rather, that the ancestral types might have been plants that had reached the level of organization of some of the early, perhaps heterosporous, ferns, and that might have retained some of the primitive psilophytic aspects. Admittedly, this suggestion is purely hypothetical, but with such an ancestral group, it would be possible to derive practically any kind of coniferophyte known, fossil or living.

Coniferophyte orders recognized in the fossil record are:

Cordaitales – Devonian (?) to Triassic (?)
Coniferales – Carboniferous to present
Taxales – Jurassic to present
Ginkgoales – Permian to present
Gnetales – Permian (?) to present

CORDAITALES

Of the Cordaitales, the Pityaceae extend back to the Lower Carboniferous and are the oldest family. It is to this family that the genus *Callixylon* had been assigned before it was known that *Callixylon* was the stem of an arborescent fernlike plant. There is, of course, no certainty that other members of the family are not vascular cryptogams, and until seeds are known, their inclusion in the Cordaitales must be on a provisional basis.

Larger specimens of *Pitys* exceed a foot and a half in diameter, and stems have a large parenchymatous pith with scattered strands of tracheids. The bulk of primary xylem is in the form of a number of mesarch bundles that are slightly embedded in the pith and separated from the secondary xylem. Leaf traces begin as single strands that divide into three at a higher level and enter the leaf in that condition. In the cortex of younger twigs are sclerotic nests. Leaves are simple and apparently fleshy, taper to a point, and are about four cm in length.

Archaeopitys is a similar genus, and according to some workers, is not easily distinguishable from *Pitys*.

The similarity of members of the Pityaceae with the Calamopityaceae of the Pteridospermales is striking. In fact, it is not impossible that there is close relationship among certain of the members, a relationship that will be more fully understood when more is known of the reproductive structures of these woody plants.

In some respects the family Poroxylaceae is more primitive than the Pityaceae, in spite of their later appearance in the geologic column. Whereas members of the Pityaceae are mesarch, primary xylem in *Poroxylon,* the only genus of the family Poroxylaceae, is exarch. Stems of the Permo-Carboniferous *Poroxylon* are exceedingly difficult to distinguish from those of the American pteridosperm *Callistophyton.* In fact, the only way to distinguish the stem of *Poroxylon* from that of *Callistophyton* is by the exarch primary xylem of the former (*Callistophyton* is mesarch). There is, however, a considerable difference in leaf structure. While the leaf of *Callistophyton* is frondlike and more than once compound, *Poroxylon* leaves are simple, thick and flat, attached with a petiole and with the lamina traversed by numerous parallel veins. It should be pointed out, however, that leaves have not been found actually attached to *Poroxylon;* those described were in close association with the stems and have striking anatomical similarities with the stems. If it eventually turns out that these detached flat leaves belong to another kind of stem, then it will be necessary to combine *Callistophyton* and *Poroxylon.* Anatomically, *Poroxylon* seems to have more in common with the pteridosperms than with the rest of the Cordaitales, and it would not be surprising if it is demonstrated that the two genera are actually one.

Members of the Cordaitaceae were large trees, perhaps 50 to 100 feet tall, branched, and with a crown of large, strap-shaped leaves. They were common trees of the Carboniferous and Permian, and large fossil logs of cordaitean trees are not uncommon in coal mines. On small branches were borne seed-bearing shoots and pollen cones. At the base was an extensive root system. Actually, much is known of these gymnospermous plants.

Although *Cordaites* is a genus name first used for leaf compressions, more of the organs of the plant were eventually included within that genus. The stem of *Cordaites* has a large pith, characteristically septate; that is, closely spaced plates of parenchymatous pith are separated by air spaces. Casts of cordaitean pith are thus easily recognizable; *Artisia,* the genus name applied to cordaitean pith casts, is marked by prominent, closely spaced lines marking the edges of the parenchyma plates at the periphery of the pith (Fig. 11-3A). Primary xylem is in small endarch bundles at the periphery of the pith; secondary xylem is compact and composed of narrow tracheids and usually narrow rays. Pitting on the radial walls of the tracheids is circular bordered, and often there are two or more rows of crowded, alternate pits on one radial wall. Around the secondary phloem is the cortex, mostly parenchymatous, but also containing sclerotic nests and secretory cavities. Leaf traces may start off singly and divide into two strands before reaching the periphery of the stele. In other instances, the leaf trace is double from its point of origin. In the cortex and leaf base the traces divide again tangentially so that a row of several strands enters the leaf.

Mesoxylon is the generic name given to certain very similar stems that have mesarch leaf traces in the stem rather than endarch traces as in *Cordaites*. In *Mesoxylon* the bundles may be endarch except in a trace that has started to bend upward and outward; in other species the mesarch condition is present for a greater distance in the stem. The distinction between these two genera seems to be an artificial one and it probably would be more natural to merge them.

Branching in *Cordaites* and *Mesoxylon* is axillary, with generally two branch traces that fuse in the outer cortex before entering the base of the lateral shoot. One species with paired axillary branches has been reported.

Leaves of cordaites are simple, linear, strap-shaped or spatulate. Venation is dichotomous, but the branches ascend so steeply that it appears almost parallel. Internally, a cross section shows veins in face view, and associated with them, often surrounding them, are sheaths of supporting sclerenchyma.

Two kinds of cordaitean petrified roots are known. One, *Amyelon,* is protostelic and exarch, with usually a triangular primary xylem core as seen in cross section. Secondary xylem is often well developed, and the outline of an older stele is cylindrical. Periderm usually surrounds the steles. *Premnoxylon* is similar in some ways; it has a pith with scattered tracheids in it, and at the periphery of the pith, and separated from the secondary xylem, are exarch primary xylem bundles. The number of these bundles varies with the diameter of the pith. In large steles, there may be seven or more primary xylem strands; in small steles, only two or three are present. In some of the smallest steles, the primary xylem is in the form of a protostele that may have three arms, as in *Amyelon*. This character has led some workers to suggest that *Amyelon* and *Premnoxylon* are congeneric, but this has not been demonstrated conclusively. The change in number of primary xylem strands in *Premnoxylon* in association with decreased size of the pith suggests that these root systems were determinate, or, at least, had a limited growth. Branch roots generally have fewer primary xylem strands than do the parent axes.

In this connection, it would seem that the stems of cordaiteans were also determinate in growth or showed a slowing down of growth near the distal extremities. Without additional thorough work this can be only a suggestion, but the wide variety of sizes of cordaitean stems that show a great range in size of pith, number of primary xylem strands, and extent of secondary xylem development would seem to indicate that branches had a more limited growth than did the parent axes.

Fruiting structures, placed in the genus *Cordaianthus,* were borne on slender branches; there are separate pollen-bearing axes and seed-bearing organs. In a pollen-bearing system, a long, slender axis bears awl-shaped bracts in two rows. In the axil of each bract is a small budlike structure with a shortened axis bearing spirally arranged, scalelike appendages (Fig. 11-1). Those scalelike structures near the tip of the bud are usually terminated by six elongated pollen sacs, and the fertile scales are in the same phyllotactic spiral as the more nearly basal sterile members. The pollen grains are surrounded by an equatorial bladder, and multicellular gametophytes are often visible within.

Ovule-bearing branches are similarly constructed. A slender axis bears axillary budlike shoots in two rows. On some of the spirally arranged members of the lateral bud are borne terminal ovules with either one or more occurring on a scale. Earlier investigators assumed that the ovule-bearing scale was actually in the axil of a small bract on the bud axis; more recent work, however, demonstrates clearly that the fertile appendages are in the same phyllotactic spiral as the sterile ones, and these ovule-bearing scales are not axillary.

The structure of *Cordaianthus,* together with a knowledge of late Paleozoic Coniferales, has played a large part in the interpreta-

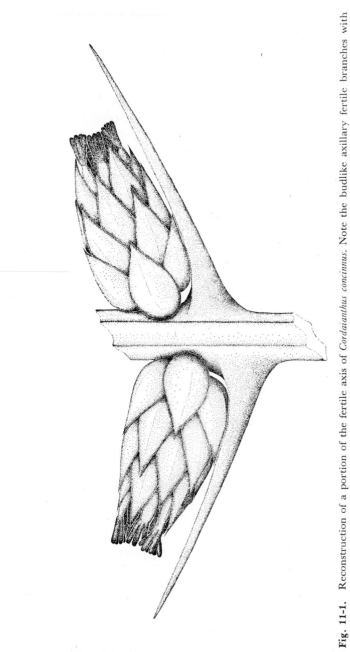

Fig. 11-1. Reconstruction of a portion of the fertile axis of *Cordaianthus concinnus*. Note the budlike axillary fertile branches with spirally arranged scales, the terminal ones of which bear elongated sporangia. (From Delevoryas, 1953.)

tion of the seed cone of conifers, long a puzzle to morphologists. A more detailed discussion on this aspect of cordaite and conifer seed cones will be presented below.

Seeds that are probably cordaitean have been found isolated, and one of the most common petrified forms is *Cardiocarpus* (note section of a *Cardiocarpus* in Fig. 9-4D). *Cardiocarpus* is flattened, bilaterally symmetrical, and in face view is roughly heart-shaped. In some species there are irregular spiny projections on the flat faces of the sclerotesta that penetrate into the fleshy, outer sarcotesta. No elaborate pollen chamber or nucellar modifications occur at the apex of the nucellus, which is free from the integuments except for attachment at the base. Gametophytes are sometimes found within the megaspore membrane, and occasionally archegonia are present.

Certain compression forms of fossil seeds assignable to the Cordaitaceae are also known. They appear to have a prominent wing around the edge of the flattened seed (reflected in the name of one genus, *Samaropsis*), but in some instances, the winglike flange may actually represent the flattened sarcotesta.

CONIFERALES

The Voltziaceae (sometimes, Voltziales) represent a group of ancient conifers that extended from the Carboniferous to the Jurassic. Some of these plants were contemporaneous with the Cordaitales. Many genera are included in this important group, most of which were arborescent, with small, spirally arranged, scalelike leaves.

Lebachia is a well-known form with pinnately arranged ultimate branches on which were borne spirally arranged leaves only a few millimeters in length (Fig. 11-2A). Leaves of *Lebachia* and of *Ernestiodendron,* a closely related form, had four stomatal bands, two long ones on the ventral side and two shorter ones on the dorsal side. Within these stomatal bands, the stomata of *Lebachia* are irregularly arranged, while in *Ernestiodendron,* one row of stomata lines each band. Another difference is the angle of divergence of the leaf; in *Lebachia,* leaves are ascending and closely appressed, while in *Ernestiodendron,* leaves are attached to the stem at roughly right angles. If it is impossible to distinguish the two

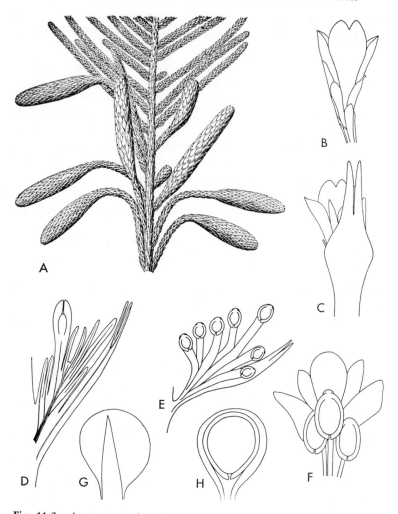

Fig. 11-2. A, reconstruction of a portion of a branch of *Lebachia piniformis* var. *Solmsii* bearing ovulate cones (upright) and microsporangiate cones (pendent). (From Florin, 1944a.) B, ovule-bearing bud of *Lebachia piniformis* viewed from the side toward the cone axis. C, lower side of bract and axillary ovule-bearing bud of *L. piniformis*. D, diagrammatic longitudinal section of fertile bud and subtending bract of *L. piniformis*. E, fertile ovuliferous bud and subtending bract of *Walchia germanica*. (B–E redrawn from Florin, 1944a.) F, ovuliferous bud of *Pseudovoltzia Liebeana*. G, lower side of a bract and ovuliferous scale of *Ullmannia Bronnii*. H, upper side of a similar ovuliferous scale. (F–H redrawn from Florin, 1944b.)

genera because of the absence of cuticle and poor preservation, such leafy twigs are placed in the artificial genus *Walchia*. *Lebachia*, *Ernestiodendron*, and *Walchia* are confined to the late Pennsylvanian and Permian.

The ovule-bearing cones of *Lebachia*, called *Gomphostrobus* when detached, are of interest and show significant similarities to *Cordaianthus*. In *Lebachia piniformis* the seed-bearing branches are cylindrical or ovoid, and the main axis consists of spirally arranged bifurcated bracts, in the axils of which are dwarf shoots (Fig. 11-2A-D). These shoots have spirally placed scalelike appendages, one of which is fertile and bears a single large terminal ovule. Thus, as in *Cordaianthus*, there is an inflorescence axis with axillary dwarf shoots. The dwarf shoots have spiral appendages, some of which are fertile. The main differences are the arrangements of the dwarf shoots (they are distichous in *Cordaianthus*) and the number of fertile scales in each dwarf shoot (only one fertile member in *Lebachia;* usually more than one in *Cordaianthus*).

Lebachia Goeppertiana is similar to *L. piniformis* in that all of the appendages of the dwarf shoot are sterile but one, and this ovule-bearing scale is on the side of the dwarf shoot away from the subtending bract.

Ernestiodendron filiciforme had inflorescence axes on which were also borne spirally arranged, bifurcated bracts. The axillary dwarf shoots, however, have three to seven appendages, all of which are fertile, each with an erect, terminal ovule. *Walchia germanica*, which may actually be an *Ernestiodendron*, is similar to *E. filiciforme,* but in this instance the terminal ovules are curved toward the inflorescence axis (Fig. 11-2E).

The Upper Permian *Pseudovoltzia Liebeana* is based on a seed-bearing cone system with dorsiventrally flattened dwarf shoots in the axils of simple, lanceolate bracts (Fig. 11-2F). The dwarf shoot has five flattened scales, and on the upper surface are three ovule-bearing stalks, each with one recurved ovule.

Ulmannia Bronnii, also from the Upper Permian, shows considerable modification of the axillary dwarf shoot (Fig. 11-2G, H). In the axil of a simple bract is an almost orbiculate scale, the result of a fusion of several sterile appendages. On the upper face is one recurved ovule. The extant *Araucaria* cone is not unlike *Ulmannia*. In *Araucaria* an ovuliferous scale (equivalent to the round scale in

Ulmannia) is borne in the axil of a bract. In *Araucaria*, however, the bract is fused to the ovuliferous scale.

It should be apparent that the structure of *Cordaianthus* and that of the seed cones in the Voltziaceae provide a key to the interpretation of coniferous cones. The series here presented — starting with *Cordaianthus*, proceeding through *Lebachia*, *Ernestio-dendron*, *Pseudovoltzia*, *Ulmannia*, and leading to extant seed cones — is not to be regarded as a straight line of evolution. Rather, these various cones are significant in showing homologies and ways in which similar structures may be variously modified. In other words, the seed cone of pine may be regarded as the morphological equivalent of a *Cordaianthus* axis and its dwarf shoots, or as homologous with a *Pseudovoltzia* cone with spirally arranged bracts and axillary, dorsiventral dwarf shoots. It is apparent, then, that a pine cone is actually a compound structure. The main cone axis is actually an inflorescence axis, and the ovule-bearing scales are actually lateral fertile branches in bract axils.

There has been subsequent modification of the seed cone among other genera of modern conifers, of course. In many cases there has been complete fusion of the bract with the subtended scale, and only an investigation of vascular structures will show the former presence of two distinct structures. In addition, not all modern conifers have only one or two seeds per ovuliferous scale, suggesting that the ancestral types of those forms could not have resembled *Ulmannia*, with only one seed per scale.

The elucidation of the structures of coniferous cones as a result of extensive studies of late Paleozoic and early Mesozoic conifers and cordaites is credited largely to Rudolf Florin, whose work represents some of the most thorough and significant paleobotanical research ever undertaken.

Certain of the Mesozoic genera of the Voltziaceae show cone scales built along the same general plan as earlier types, but often exhibiting various kinds of modifications. In the Lower Triassic *Voltzia*, each dwarf shoot consists of five flattened and fused scales, resembling the structure in *Pseudovoltzia*, but the three fertile members are actually fused to the upper surface of the dorsiventral sterile members. *Schizolepis*, from the Upper Triassic and Lower Jurassic, is similar, but has only three fused sterile scales. Further-more, the axes of the fertile appendages are adnate and also fused laterally to each other at their bases.

Palissya is found in the Upper Triassic and Lower Jurassic, and its ovuliferous scale consists of about ten distichously arranged ovule-bearing axes in the axil of a large bract (Fig. 11-4A). Each ovule is not quite erect, but is partially bent back. Furthermore, it does not appear as if the fertile complex is fused to the bract. *Stachyotaxus*, of the same age, is similar but considerably reduced; only two ovules are borne on the forked ovuliferous axillary structure (Fig. 11-4B).

Pollen-bearing cones in the Voltziaceae were borne on the tips of some of the small branches. Unlike the seed cones, the pollen cones were simple, consisting only of a cone axis with spirally arranged microsporophylls. In their organization, then, microsporangiate cones did not correspond to the structure of cordaitean pollen-bearing axes.

Other conifers of the Upper Carboniferous and Lower Permian are important in adding to a knowledge of the vegetative structure of early members of the Coniferales. Although conifer leaves are generally simple and, especially in the Coniferales, provided with but a single vein, many primitive coniferophytes had dissected foliage. *Carpentieria*, from the Lower Permian (Fig. 11-4C), has stem axes covered with slender, spirally arranged, bifurcated leaves, a condition reflected only in the ovulate cone of such forms as *Lebachia* or *Ernestiodendron*. According to Florin, the *Lebachia*, *Walchia*, and *Ernestiodendron* leaves are reduced from a *Carpentieria*-type of construction. Although the blade of the leaf of the Lower Permian *Buriardia* is simple, the single vein that enters the base of the leaf dichotomizes one or more times, and the tip of the leaf is lobed. In the more ultimate branches, however, the leaves are simply bifurcated.

Some anatomical observations have been possible on stems of late Paleozoic members of the Voltziaceae. All have pith, small endarch primary xylem bundles, and compact secondary xylem, with little or no xylem parenchyma and no resin canals. Faint growth rings are sometimes visible.

A number of petrified coniferophyte stems described from Upper Carboniferous and Permian deposits of South America show that the order Coniferales was actually widespread even at that time. Furthermore, they emphasize the difficulty in deriving the Coniferales from the Cordaitales, since both groups existed at the same time.

Fig. 11-3. A, pith cast (*Artisia*) of a cordaitean stem axis. B, longitudinal section of *Araucaria mirabilis*, a Mesozoic cone from Patagonia.

Subsequent evolution of coniferalean lines since the Paleozoic is not clearly agreed upon. Some workers believe that the Pinaceae are the oldest of living conifers, while others hold that the Araucariaceae are the most primitive. The fossil record does not present answers to this question, but it does demonstrate various lines of specialization manifested today by the diverse contemporary coniferalean families.

Evidence used to substantiate the suggested antiquity of the Araucariaceae is the presence of wood with araucarian features continuous in an almost unbroken line from the Paleozoic to the present. Araucarian wood possesses closely spaced circular bordered pits in alternate rows on radial walls of tracheids. The famous Petrified Forest National Monument in Arizona has tremendous numbers of petrified gymnospermous logs that are Upper Triassic in age. These silicified trunks have typical araucarian wood struc-

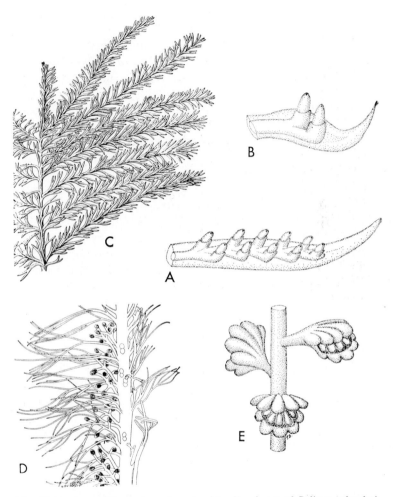

Fig. 11-4. A, ovuliferous branch and subtending bract of *Palissya sphenolepis.*
B, *Stachyotaxus elegans,* ovuliferous branch and subtending bract. (A and B
redrawn from Hirmer, 1936.) C, portion of the shoot system of *Carpentieria
frondosa.* (From Florin, 1944a.) D, portion of shoot of *Trichopitys heteromorpha*
showing dichotomously branched leaves and axillary ovuliferous short shoots.
(From Florin, 1949.) E, reconstruction of a portion of a fertile shoot of *Leptostrobus longus.* (Redrawn and modified from Harris, 1951.)

ture and are actually placed in the genus *Araucarioxylon*. This in itself, however, is not conclusive proof of the existence of plants that were relatives of the extinct araucarias.

Woodworthia, from the same area, is another genus of petrified trunks with araucarian pitting, but embedded in the large masses of secondary wood are persistent short shoots, suggesting possible pinaceous affinities.

Twigs found throughout the Mesozoic and resembling to some degree the vegetative features of *Araucaria* have been placed in the genus *Pagiophyllum*. These branches are covered with spirally arranged, overlapping, triangular leaves. No reproductive structures are attached, and the resemblance to *Araucaria* is based on superficial similarity.

Other *Araucaria*-like remains occur in the Cretaceous, and it seems likely that there is a definite affinity between certain of these and members of the modern Araucariaceae.

Beautifully preserved silicified cones of *Araucaria* have been described from Patagonia in deposits whose age is not definite, although it is probable that the rocks are late Mesozoic or early Tertiary. Originally named *Proaraucaria*, cones of these deposits are so like the modern *Araucaria* that they have been included within the modern genus (Fig. 11-3B).

The Pinaceae may extend back to the late Triassic-early Jurassic, but the oldest remains of the family are not always convincingly like pinaceous members. Seeds and pollen grains with bladders like those in modern forms have been reported from the late Triassic-early Jurassic. By the Cretaceous, however, the family was well established, being represented by cones and pollen as well as by vegetative remains.

The interesting Cretaceous genus *Prepinus*, which is based on dwarf shoots, has been assigned to the Pinaceae. These short shoots are not as reduced as are modern pinaceous brachyblasts, but each was somewhat shorter than 1 cm in length and bore about 20 terminal needles. Furthermore, the short shoot was terminated by a bud that contributed to growth in length, as in the dwarf shoots of *Larix*. The presence of a sturdy short shoot is considerably more primitive than the situation in modern pines, where the short shoots lack terminal buds and where only a few needles, sometimes only one, are borne on the dwarf branch.

Seed cones of the Pinaceae are abundant in Cretaceous and later deposits.

A significant Lower Cretaceous wood, *Brachyoxylon brachyphylloides*, originally called *Telephragmoxylon*, exhibits an anatomical feature that seems to suggest the possible origin of axial parenchyma in xylem. At the ends of growth rings certain tracheids are septate, but individual cells conform to the original tracheid outline and are nonliving at maturity. The situation in *B. brachyphylloides* is more primitive than a further step in the evolution of xylem parenchyma, seen in the root wood of *Picea*, where some of the members of the septate tracheids remain living. Finally, in the establishment of xylem parenchyma, all members of the septate member remain alive.

The Taxodiaceae are another old family of conifers extending back to the Jurassic or earlier. Sterile shoots of the genus *Elatocladus* from the Jurassic or before may actually represent taxodiaceous remains. Cones very much like those of the modern *Sequoia* are known from the Jurassic. An interesting new genus, *Parataxodium*, has been described from the Upper Cretaceous of Alaska. *Parataxodium* has distichous, alternate leaves borne on short shoots that occur in axils of alternate leaves on long shoots. Ovulate and pollen cones are also preserved.

One of the most interesting series of events in recent times involves the discovery of another taxodiaceous genus, *Metasequoia*, from the Tertiary of Japan. A few years after the discovery of the fossil forms, living trees of this new genus were found for the first time in China. It is a rare event in botanical history for the discovery of the fossil genus to precede the recognition of the modern counterpart.

TAXALES

The Taxales were a distinct order at least as far back as the Jurassic period, when a variety of forms lived. Furthermore, forms included in the genus *Taxus* have been described from rocks Jurassic in age. *Torreya* also occurs in similar deposits. Some of the fossil members of the Taxales, however, suggest the former existence of more than just one family, the Taxaceae.

GINKGOALES

The Ginkgoales represent a relict order of gymnospermous plants with a past history indicating that it was once a flourishing and widespread group of plants. It is an assemblage of plants that seem to have characters of both the Cycadophyta and the other Coniferophyta. Fossils that seem referable to the order are known from the Mesozoic and possibly before, and there also existed at that time other forms that seem to show affinity with the Ginkgoales. Reports of still older ginkgophytes are based on remains of fan-shaped leaves having a superficial resemblance to the *Ginkgo* leaf. These reports of Carboniferous and Devonian ginkgophytes, however, are not free from question.

Trichopitys, a plant from the Lower Permian, was quite conceivably on the ginkgophyte line of evolution (Fig. 11-4D). Axes of *Trichopitys* bear spirally arranged leaves that are without laminae and that dichotomized several times. In the axils of some of the leaves are small branch systems, with each branch terminated by a recurved ovule. Ovules usually range from four to six in number. This fertile "truss" is the equivalent of the ovule-bearing stalk in *Ginkgo* that, in modern forms, is confined to the dwarf shoot.

Czekanowskia is a problematical fossil, Jurassic in age, that has certain ginkgophyte characters, but yet does not fit the order in certain of its other features. On short branches are borne clusters of long, slender leaves, ten or more in number, that dichotomized two or three times. Fruiting axes in the genus *Leptostrobus* (Fig. 11-4E), which apparently were attached to *Czekanowskia* foliage, are even less *Ginkgo*-like than the sterile branches. In *Leptostrobus,* the base of the slender fertile axis is clothed with spirally placed scale leaves. Loosely arranged above are pairs of lobed, concave, valvelike structures, with the concavities facing each other. Within the concavity of each valve are usually five ovules, with pollen grains in close association.

Sphenobaiera is a primitive ginkgophyte that extended back to the Permian. Its leaves are dichotomously branched, with no laminae, and they were borne on both long and dwarf shoots. If, indeed, these plants were ginkgophytes, the microsporangiate structures show what may have been a primitive condition compared with modern *Ginkgo* microsporophylls. In *Sphenobaiera* the slender microsporophylls were borne in short shoots; each microsporophyll is branched with the ultimate members forked and each member bearing three to five sporangia.

Baiera is a genus of Mesozoic ginkgophytes, the leaves of which closely intergrade with those of *Ginkgoites*. Leaves of *Baiera* are fan-shaped and deeply incised, and the blade often tapers toward the stem, resulting in an almost sessile leaf. Associated with one species, *B. Muensteriana* from the Jurassic, are microsporangium-bearing axes. These axes are slender and catkinlike, and bear small stalks terminated by ten to twelve sporangia. Seed-bearing stalks have also been found associated with these *Baiera* leaves, but their connection is even more uncertain.

Ginkgoites has a somewhat more distinct petiole, and the leaves range in shape from those with extremely divided laminae to forms approaching the typical entire leaf of the *Ginkgo* short shoot. Of course, almost the same range of leaf types can be found on a single *Ginkgo* tree.

It is quite evident from the fossil record of the ginkgophytes that the group once had a wide geographical range. In Mesozoic and Tertiary deposits, ginkgophyte remains make up a conspicuous part of the floral assemblages.

GNETALES

The small order Gnetales left a very meager fossil record, and almost nothing is known concerning the origin and subsequent evolution of the group. A further complication is that among modern botanists there is uncertainty as to whether the group is even a natural one. On the basis of fossil pollen, it seems that the order was in existence during the Permian; in deposits of that period *Ephedra*- and *Welwitschia*-like pollen grains are found.

REFERENCES

ARNOLD, C. A., and J. S. LOWTHER, 1955. "A new Cretaceous conifer from northern Alaska," *Amer. J. Botan.*, **42**: 522–528.

BAXTER, R. W., 1959. "A new cordaitean stem with paired axillary branches," *Amer. J. Botan.*, **46**: 163–169.

Bertrand, C. E., 1899. "Les poroxylons végétaux fossiles de l'époque houillière," *Ann. Soc. Belg. Microsc.*, **13**, fasc. 1: 5–49.

———, and B. Renault, 1886. "Recherches sur les poroxylons," *Arch. Botan. Nord France*, **2**: 243–389.

Calder, Mary G., 1953. "A coniferous petrified forest in Patagonia," *Bull. Brit. Mus. (Nat. Hist.) Geol.*, **2**: 99–138.

Cohen, Lila M., and T. Delevoryas, 1959. "An occurrence of *Cordaites* in the Upper Pennsylvanian of Illinois," *Amer. J. Botan.*, **46**: 545–549.

Daugherty, L. H., 1941. "The Upper Triassic flora of Arizona," *Carnegie Inst. Washington Publ.*, **526**: 1–108.

Delevoryas, T., 1953. "A new male córdaitean fructification from the Kansas Carboniferous," *Amer. J. Botan.*, **40**: 144–150.

Florin, R., 1944a. "Die Koniferen des Oberkarbons und des unteren Perms. Part 6," *Palaeontographica*, **85B**: 365–456.

———, 1944b. "Die Koniferen des Oberkarbons und des unteren Perms. Part 7," *Palaeontographica*, **85B**: 457–654.

———, 1949. "The morphology of *Trichopitys heteromorpha* Saporta, a seed-plant of Palaeozoic age, and the evolution of the female flowers in the Ginkgoinae," *Acta Horti Bergiani*, **15**: 79–109.

———, 1950. "On female reproductive organs in the Cordaitinae," *Acta Horti Bergiani*, **15**: 111–134.

———, 1951. "Evolution in cordaites and conifers," *Acta Horti Bergiani*, **15**: 285–388.

———, 1958. "On Jurassic taxads and conifers from north-western Europe and eastern Greenland," *Acta Horti Bergiani*, **17**: 257–402.

Fry, W. L., 1956. "New cordaitean cones from the Pennsylvanian of Iowa," *J. Paleont.*, **30**: 35–45.

Gordon, W. T., 1935. "The genus *Pitys*, Witham, emend.," *Trans. Roy. Soc. Edinburgh*, **58**: 279–311.

Harris, T. M., 1951. "The fructification of *Czekanowskia* and its allies," *Phil. Trans. Roy. Soc. London*, **235B**: 483–508.

Hirmer, M., 1936. "Die Blüten der Coniferen. I. Entwicklungsgeschichte und vergleichende Morphologie des weiblichen Blütenzapfens der Coniferen," *Bibliotheca Botanica*, **114** (1): 1–100.

Jeffrey, E. C., 1908. "On the structure of the leaf in Cretaceous pines," *Ann. Botan.*, **22**: 208–220.

Kräusel, R., and E. Dolianiti, 1958. "Gymnospermenhölzer aus dem Paläozoikum Brasiliens," *Palaeontographica*, **104B**: 115–137.

Miki, S., 1941. "On the change of flora in eastern Asia since Tertiary period. (I), the clay or lignite beds in Japan with special reference to the *Pinus trifolia* beds in central Hondo," *Jap. J. Botan.*, **11**: 237–303.

Pierce, R. L., and J. W. Hall, 1953. "*Premnoxylon*, a new cordaitean axis," *Phytomorphology*, **3**: 384–391.

Roth, E. A., 1955. "The anatomy and modes of preservation of the genus *Cardiocarpus spinatus* Graham," *Univ. Kansas Sci. Bull.*, **37**: 151–174.

Torrey, R. E., 1921. "*Telephragmoxylon* and the origin of wood parenchyma," *Ann. Botan.*, **35**: 73–77.

TRAVERSE, A., 1950. "The primary vascular body of *Mesoxylon Thompsonii*, a new American cordaitalean," *Amer. J. Botan.*, **37**: 318–325.

WIELAND, G. R., 1935. *The Cerro Cuadrado Petrified Forest*, Washington, D.C.: Carnegie Inst.

chapter twelve ❯ Subdivision
Pteropsida, Class
Angiospermophyta

It is to paleobotany that most botanists hopefully turn for the answer to the perplexing problem of the origin of the group of plants most important to human economy. The angiosperms are currently the most widespread group of higher plants that have become adapted to an extreme range of habitats.

While the fossil record has nothing to contribute at the present concerning *the* ancestor (or ancestors?) of the flowering plants, there are some interesting forms among the extinct plants that show the possible origin of the angiospermous habit (that is, seeds enclosed within a carpel).

It has already been pointed out how the cupulate pteridosperms present an interesting morphological condition suggestive of a seed-enclosing organ. Structures such as those found in *Calathospermum* and *Gnetopsis* are examples of Paleozoic cupules surrounding several seeds (Fig. 12-1A, B). A closing over of the open distal portion of the cupule would produce a structure closely resembling a carpel with basal placentation of ovules.

Mesozoic peltasperms and corystosperms also show the development of hooded structures with ovules within, again suggesting resemblances to angiosperms. And the Caytoniaceae, which caused such a stir at the time of their discovery, are still impressive plants,

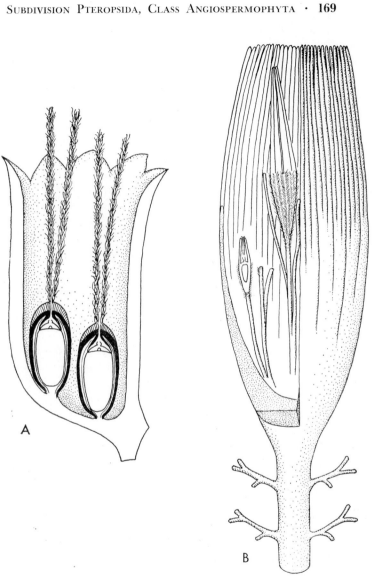

Fig. 12-1. A, cupule of *Gnetopsis elliptica* with two ovules. (Redrawn from Andrews, 1948, by permission of Univ. of Chicago Press.) B, partially sectioned cupule of *Calathospermum fimbriatum* showing two of the enclosed ovules. (Redrawn from Barnard, 1960.)

with structures as close to carpels as are found among certain angiosperms (some angiosperms have carpels that are incompletely closed, allowing pollen to enter the ovary and germinate within). It must be realized, however, that more than just a simple carpel is necessary to make an angiosperm. Even though certain seed ferns have structures resembling carpels that may even have come about in the same way as did angiospermous carpels, there are other conditions necessary to an angiosperm precursor that the pteridosperms do not meet. For example, the stamens of angiosperms are quite distinct from anything in seed ferns. In the pteridosperms the microsporangia were generally part of an extensive leaf system. The stamen of a flower is theoretically the morphological equiv alent of an entire pteridosperm frond. Of course, this homology may be possible, considering the tremendous reduction of a fertile seed fern frond in the evolution of the megasporophyll of *Zamia*, but nothing exists in the fossil record to suggest that stamens had such an origin.

Another difficulty in considering the seed ferns as angiosperm precursors is the great difference they show in secondary xylem. Primitive angiosperms supposedly have scalariform secondary thickenings, but the pteridosperms most often have closely spaced circular bordered pits, similar in some ways to the pitting in some of the supposedly advanced angiosperms.

As mentioned earlier, however, one may be facing a dilemma if in his search for angiosperm ancestors he brings preconceived ideas as to what such an ancestor should look like rather than by interpreting the fossils for what they are.

Recent work on *Glossopteris* and its related fertile parts suggested that these unusual plants were angiosperms of the late Paleozoic and early Mesozoic. The saclike structures in one of the concave valves of *Scutum* were interpreted as simple pistils, but the preservation does not warrant such conclusions. It is conceivable, however, that the two halves of the hinged valve of *Scutum* could have some similarity to a primitive carpel.

For many years it was hoped that the cones of the Cycadeoidales would provide a clue to the origin of angiospermous flowers. Cones of *Cycadeoidea*, especially, which had originally been thought to be flowerlike with a basal perianth of spiral bracts, a whorl of large expanded microsporophylls, and the ovule-bearing portions in the center, were thought to have resemblances to certain large, primitive flowers such as those of *Magnolia*. According to proponents of this view, the carpel was derived in possibly more than one way from the ovulate receptacle of *Cycadeoidea*. One view would interpose a stage with leaflike megasporophylls, with the ovules borne on the edges, between the cycadeoid cone structure and true closed carpels. Such a stage, however, was entirely hypothetical. Another view would derive a carpel simply by overlapping some of the interseminal scales over the ovules, completely closing them in. Again, this is completely hypothetical, and it is difficult to find among angiosperms any carpellate conditions that in any way resemble the situation just described.

More recent work on the cycadeoid cone, however, has shown that in *Cycadeoidea* there are no such things as expanded microsporophylls, and thus it would tax the imagination to derive angiosperm stamens from such a compound synangium. Williamsonian microsporophylls are somewhat different, but again they represent compound synangia: microsporophylls are fused at the base, and the pollen sacs are actually composed of more than one sporangium. The Cycadeoidales, then, while an important group in earlier theories concerning the evolution of the flower, upon closer examination present insurmountable difficulties if they are to be considered precursors of angiosperms.

Indisputable angiosperm remains from the Mesozoic do not help to solve the problem concerning the origin of this great group. As soon as a fossil is recognizable as a true angiosperm, there is no difference between it and a modern counterpart. Furthermore, not enough is known of earliest angiosperm floras to give a positive clue concerning the relative primitiveness of the various modern angiosperm families.

The very fragmentary nature of the remains adds to the difficulties connected with earliest fossil angiosperms. Leaves, for example, are the most abundant megascopic angiosperm remains, but a knowledge of the structure of an early Cretaceous leaf resembling *Ficus* tells nothing about the fructifications of the plant on which it was borne, or whether the flowers had actually attained the angiospermous level of evolution. Unless flower parts, seeds, and fruits are known, there can be no certainty that the plants in question are actually angiosperms simply because the leaf is "angiospermous." In other words, it is not unlikely that different plant organs evolved at different rates, and the leaf conceivably could have evolved at a much faster (or slower) rate than did the reproductive parts. Similarly, the angiospermous condition could have evolved first in the reproductive parts in plants that have extremely primitive leaves and vascular anatomy.

It is because of such difficulties that paleobotanists cannot be certain about the earliest fossil angiosperms unless many parts of the plant are preserved. Some of the earliest supposed angiosperm remains are pollen grains, but simply because these grains closely approximate pollen in living angiosperms they are not proof in themselves of the actual existence of angiospermous plants in the age represented by the rocks in which the pollen occurs.

Perhaps these comments suggest an overly pessimistic point of view on the part of the author with respect to hopes of uncovering fossil evidence that will help to solve the mystery of the origin of angiosperms. Such is not the case; rather, these remarks simply serve to remind paleobotanists and others that different organs of a plant evolve at different rates and that there is no reason to believe that in the course of plant evolution a complete angiosperm suddenly appeared. There must have been, instead, a gradual series of processes, with certain organs attaining the condition in modern angiosperms before others.

In spite of the problems involved in recognizing what the earliest angiosperm might have looked like, the fossil record will probably be the most important guide in attempts to solve the perplexing problem of angiosperm origin.

The earliest angiospermlike plants are found in Triassic rocks. One of the most significant finds in recent times was the discovery of palmlike leaves from the Triassic of Colorado. These leaves, placed in the genus *Sanmiguelia*, have no organic material preserved, but the leaf closely resembles that of a palm, with a stout petiole and pleated lamina. Critics of this interpretation insist that without organic remains, *Sanmiguelia* cannot actually be shown to be a palm, but some of these same workers would not hesitate to call it a palm if similarly preserved specimens had been found in the Tertiary. As mentioned above, the existence of a palm leaf in itself is not sufficient evidence to indicate that the plant had an angiospermous type of reproduction, but there is no denying that the fossil looks more like a palm than anything else.

Another Triassic plant fragment with possible angiosperm affinities is *Furcula granulifer*. The specimens consist of portions of leaves up to 15 cm in length that forked once. Epidermal characters and venation resemble those of dicotyledonous leaves. Because of its very fragmentary nature and because net venation does not always imply angiosperm affinities, the significance of *Furcula* remains uncertain.

Jurassic palmlike leaf impressions have also been described from France, and until it can be conclusively proved that the interpretation of these fossils is in error, these reports may stand as further evidence for the presence of angiosperms in the Jurassic period.

A variety of pollen grains with supposed angiosperm affinities have been described from the Jurassic, but in many cases these have been shown to be gymnospermous pollen grains or, in other cases, fern spores. There have even been reports of Carboniferous angiosperm pollen grains, but these reports must await final interpretation.

It is in the Lower Cretaceous that fossil remains with modern angiosperm counterparts make their dramatic appearance. Subsequent to the appearance of angiosperms in the Lower Cretaceous there occurred a rapid and widespread distribution of the flowering plants. By the end of the Cretaceous, most of the fossil floras from all parts of the world had angiosperm representatives.

The actual geographic origin of angiosperms and subsequent migration patterns are not fully understood. One prominent idea is that the flowering plants had their origins in equatorial regions and that subsequent distribution was poleward in both hemispheres. Such a pattern of distribution would seem quite plausible, but before it can be accepted without question it is necessary for investigators to learn more about Cretaceous equatorial, Arctic, and Antarctic floral assemblages.

It is not the purpose here to discuss subsequent angiosperm distribution, but a few words on the record of climatic changes left by the fossils are of interest. Assuming that the physiological requirements of ancient angiosperms were the same as those necessary for modern relatives, it is possible to reconstruct the environment in which the fossil plants lived.

The presence in the Pacific Northwest of late Eocene and early Oligocene floras containing such plants as figs, laurels, cinnamon, avocado, and magnolia suggests that a subtropical climate prevailed at that time. In Gulf state deposits of the same age plants have been found whose nearest relatives now live in tropical South America and coastal Mexico, again suggesting a relative warming of the earth. In Alaska and Greenland at that time lived such trees as maple, beech, oak, sycamore, and basswood — plants now living in temperate climates. The warming, then, apparently had extended northward, and plants that could not now survive in such Arctic sites were flourishing there in the late Eocene.

Toward the end of the Oligocene there had been a slight cooling reflected by the replacing of subtropical elements in the Pacific Northwest by warm temperate types such as *Metasequoia*, maple, alder, dogwood, oak, hazel, and sycamore. Warm temperate plants also replaced the subtropical types in the Dakotas and Montana.

During the middle to late Miocene there was a slight reversal of the cooling trend, with subtropical elements again migrating northward. The warming at this time, however, was not to the degree it had been during the late Eocene and early Oligocene.

By the late Pliocene, climatic zones approached those of the present time, but before the present, the earth was to undergo the several severe climatic fluctuations induced by glaciation.

The presence of fossil plants in Arctic and Antarctic regions has led to speculation concerning the cause of climatic shifting. One prominent idea, supported largely by European paleobotanists, is that the poles of the earth were not stable but migrated. If this were true, it is possible that Alaska or Greenland could have been situated in less severe climatic zones in earlier times. A slight shifting of the pole in the late Oligocene would have resulted in some cooling of these regions, and so on. A shifting of the poles is difficult to imagine, however, because while a replaced pole could account for the fossil floras of one hemisphere, those of the same age and at the same latitude in another hemisphere would be placed in hazardous environments. The climatic shifts, as reflected in Tertiary floras, seem to have been circumpolar, and a migrating of the poles is not demonstrated by this circumstance.

A simple explanation for milder climates at polar latitudes is on the basis of a slight elevation of sea level. A sea level about 200 feet higher than it is at present would make profound changes in continental climates. And if polar temperatures were tolerable by plants, an extremely wide variety of plant forms could exist and reproduce there because every conceivable kind of natural photoperiod is present in these latitudes at some time of the year. Although the fossil record at present has not contributed much information concerning the source of angiosperms, much has been learned about what has happened to the group since it made its appearance. Even though investigators are still in the dark about the time and mode of origin of flowering plants, the study of fossils will doubtlessly provide the key to the problem eventually.

REFERENCES

ANDREWS, H. N., JR., 1948. "Some evolutionary trends in the pteridosperms," *Botan. Gaz.*, 110: 13–31.

AXELROD, D. I., 1952. "A theory of angiosperm evolution," *Evolution*, 6: 29–60.

———, 1958. "Evolution of the Madro-Tertiary geoflora," *Botan. Rev.*, 24: 433–509.

———, 1959. "Poleward migration of early angiosperm floras," *Science*, 130: 203–207.

———, 1961. "How old are the angiosperms?" *Amer. J. Sci.*, 259: 447–459.

BARNARD, P. D. W., 1960. "*Calathospermum fimbriatum* sp. nov., a Lower Carboniferous pteridosperm cupule from Scotland," *Palaeontology*, 3: 265–275.

BROWN, R. W., 1956. "Palmlike plants from the Dolores formation (Triassic) of southwestern Colorado," *U.S. Geol. Survey Prof. Paper*, 274-H: 205–209.

ERDTMANN, G., 1948. "Did dicotyledonous plants exist in early Jurassic times?" *Geol. Fören. Stockholm Förhandl.*, 70: 265–271.

HARRIS, T. M., 1932. "The fossil flora of Scoresby Sound East Greenland. Part 2: Description of seed plants *incertae sedis* together with a discussion of certain cycadophyte cuticles," *Medd. Grønland*, 85 (3): 1–112.

———, 1960. "The origin of angiosperms," *Adv. Sci.*, 67: 1–7.

HUGHES, N. F., and R. A. COUPER, 1958. "Palynology of the Brora coal of the Scottish Middle Jurassic," *Nature*, 181: 1482–1483.

LIGNIER, O., 1908. "Nouvelles recherches sur le *Propalmophyllum liasinum* Lignier," *Mem. Soc. Linn. Normandie*, 23: 1–14.

SCOTT, R. A., E. S. BARGHOORN, and ESTELLA B. LEOPOLD, 1960. "How old are the angiosperms?" *Amer. J. Sci.*, 258-A: 284–299.

SIMPSON, J. B., 1937. "Fossil pollen in Scottish Jurassic coal," *Nature*, 139: 673.

WOLFE, J. A., and E. S. BARGHOORN, 1960. "Generic change in Tertiary floras in relation to age," *Amer. J. Sci.*, 258-A: 388–399.

chapter thirteen ⋮ Summary and
Conclusions

The panorama of plant change through the ages has been a varied and exciting one. The assemblage of plants in a temperate hardwood forest, the diversified and exotic plants in a tropical rain forest, an alpine plant community, and a desert assemblage of plants have no similarity with forests of the late Devonian or of the Permian or of the Triassic, yet each of these communities is the result of a series of evolutionary changes in plants that existed during past ages. In many cases the record of these evolutionary changes recorded in the rocks is remarkably clear; in more cases, it is still incomplete. In spite of the imperfections of the record, it is possible to discern various lines of evolution, and even the incomplete record is sometimes enough to remove our suggested evolutionary schemes from the realm of pure speculation to one in which the available facts fit in with the suggested theories. We have learned the approximate times of appearance of various major groups of plants, and some of the subsequent developments among them, including the extinction of some.

From a study of paleobotany it has become apparent that simple plants existed in the Precambrian, and these remains suggest affinities with the blue-green algae and with the fungi. It has also become evident that many of the various algal groups are represented by fossils as far back as the early Paleozoic, suggesting that these algal lines have been independent for some time. True, the fossil record has not yet supplied information on physiological differences among the fossil algae, differences that play an important part in the classification of algae today. Nevertheless, it is not possible to disregard morphological characters, many of which have been faithfully preserved and that are significant enough to demonstrate several algal lines in the Paleozoic. Modern systems of classification reflect this paleobotanical evidence.

It is more difficult, on the basis of paleobotany alone, to prove which group of algae was the source of land plants; the choice of the Chlorophyta as the source is based largely on a knowledge of contemporary forms. Among the various kinds of green algae are morphological and physiological characteristics that must have preceded the evolution of the Embryophyta. Prerequisites are alternation of generations, with oogamous sexual reproduction; proper pigments and reserve foods; bulky, three-dimensional, parenchymatous body. Not one green alga has all of these characters, but they are combined within the entire division among various forms.

Although some paleobotanists would disagree, many believe that the simplest land vascular plant was a naked, green, dichotomously constructed plant having sporangia at the tips of some of the slender branches. Except for the presence of vascular tissue and cuticle, the general structure was probably quite algalike. The naked axes were photosynthetic, and a slender, simple conducting strand traversed the center of each axis. These plants would have had no roots; anchoring and absorbing would have been effected by some of the branch systems.

This type of plant structure is found in a large number of earlier plants, in the Silurian and Devonian periods. Among the Psilophytales, a number of plants with this simple type of structure are known.

From a group of plants such as this could have arisen more specialized groups, such as the Lycopsida, Sphenopsida, and Pteropsida. This specialization must have occurred early in the Paleozoic, perhaps in the Ordovician or even in the Cambrian period because by late Silurian times there is evidence of the coexistence of some of the more specialized groups with members of the Psilophytales. This should be no reason to doubt the ancestral nature of psilophytic plants if one simply regards the known Psilophytales as a group that continued to persist for some time, even after more highly advanced forms had become differentiated from it earlier.

Members of the Lycopsida could conceivably owe their origins to psilophytelike ancestors. The general construction of the earliest lycopsids is that of a dichotomous plant body, with horizontal, dichotomizing anchoring and absorbing stems and upright, also dichotomous, aerial axes. Closely spaced scalelike leaves covered the aerial stems, and these leaves might be regarded as homologous with the veinless scales of *Asteroxylon* or *Psilophyton*. Another interpretation is that the leaves are much reduced lateral branches that were once part of the "telomic" branching of a primitive psilophytic plant. It is actually simpler to regard the leaves as modified enations, but to explain the adaxial position of sporangia on that basis is difficult.

From these early Paleozoic herbaceous lycopsids developed massive, arborescent forms that flourished in the late Paleozoic. Herbaceous types, too, persisted. The modern *Lycopodium, Phylloglossum,* and *Selaginella* are vestiges of the herbaceous lines, while *Isoetes* and *Stylites* might be regarded as extremely reduced lycopsids that had their origin among some of the treelike members of the Paleozoic. An interesting series can be traced through the Mesozoic to forms like *Isoetes* and *Stylites*.

Of considerable interest among the Lycopsida is the development of the seed habit. *Lepidocarpon* has a sporangium (comparable to the nucellus of a seed) surrounded by a modified sporophyll (integument), with a single functional megaspore within the sporangium. *Miadesmia* shows a similar structure among herbaceous lycopsids. Although *Lepidocarpon* and *Miadesmia* may be regarded as functional seeds, these plants probably had nothing to do with the evolution of seeds in other groups of vascular plants.

It has been possible to demonstrate that fossil arborescent lycopsids had an almost determinate growth habit. Naturally, the sporeling had a slender primary vascular strand, but this expanded considerably higher in the main trunk, changing from a protostele below to a siphonostele above. Secondary xylem was thicker near the base than at higher levels. Branches, however, had a smaller primary xylem strand than that of the parent axis, and still more distal branches had even smaller primary xylem cylinders. Ultimate branches had small protostelic strands. Secondary xylem development also dwindled toward the extremities. Leaves and leaf bases are smaller on the ultimate branches than on the larger axes; the number of rows of leaves also decreased distally. A similar habit of growth is found in some present-day species of *Lycopodium*. Early Paleozoic sphenopsids also retain a number of psilophytic characters even though in other respects they show structures typical of the articulates. Although leaves and branches are whorled, these appendages retain a dichotomous structure; a possible Silurian sphenopsid, *Protohyenia*, demonstrates an earlier condition, in which appendages had not become definitely whorled. It seems probable that leaves in the Sphenopsida derived from minor branch systems that eventually became reduced to small, scalelike structures (for example, *Equisetum*).

The evolution of the sphenopsid sporangiophore is well documented by fossil forms. A dichotomously branched telomic system with terminal sporangia might have served as the starting point. There followed a shortening of the terminal, sporangium-bearing branches, with an accompanying recurvation of the sporangia. *Hyenia* and *Calamophyton* show such a sporangiophore structure. Finally, the sporangial branches were considerably shortened, and the recurved sporangia were attached distally to a fleshy mass of tissue that in some forms became conspicuously peltate.

Represented by only a single genus at the present time, the Sphenopsida reached their greatest development in the Carboniferous and Permian periods when the members of the group attained considerable height and underwent massive secondary vascular development. Like the Lycopsida, the Sphenopsida seem to exhibit limited growth, with lateral branches smaller than the parent axes from which they arose, and with less potentiality for massive growth than the main axis.

The transition from the Psilophytales to primitive, fernlike plants is an easy one. Early fernlike forms such as *Protopteridium* retained a dichotomous, or somewhat sympodial, method of branching, but the distal extremities of the branches show the beginning of fronds. These fronds probably originated from a planation of the terminal branchlets, followed by a webbing between the axes to produce a definite, leaflike structure.

Some of the early fernlike plants developed secondary xylem and phloem and grew to tree size. Leaves, however, still retained certain primitive characteristics such as dichotomous venation, often with incomplete webbing, so that the structure of the leaf was a flattened dichotomous system.

From this Devonian fern complex developed a variety of kinds of ferns and possibly even seed plants. One group of ferns, the Coenopteridales, is primitive in certain respects (for example, it has a three-dimensional leaf with sometimes little distinction from the stem) and quite specialized in others (for example, peculiar petiole traces). The order probably had little to do with the origin of other groups of ferns. Fern families related to modern types were evident in the Carboniferous, with progressively more appearing later in the fossil record. Early families with modern relatives are Schizaeaceae, Gleicheniaceae, Psaroniaceae (related to Marattiaceae), and Osmundaceae. Members of the Psaroniaceae were large trees with complex, polycyclic, dictyostelic stems covered with a thick mantle of adventitious roots. Synangia closely resemble some of the modern marattiaceous fructifications. The Paleozoic Schizaeaceae and Gleicheniaceae also had sporangia closely approximating those of their modern counterparts. An impressive record exists demonstrating the intrastelar origin of pith in the Osmundaceae.

With a few notable exceptions, Mesozoic fern families were quite similar to those of today. *Tempskya* was an arborescent Cretaceous fern with a false stem consisting of many amphiphloic siphonostelic stems held together among a mass of adventitious roots.

It is probable that the first seed plants, members of the Pteridospermales, did not arise from the ferns but from a group of plants with some fernlike characters and many simpler, psilophytic features as well. Secondary vascular tissues probably were also present in these ancestors. Plants that perhaps fulfill the requirements for such precursors are some of the Cladoxylales, *Tetra-xylopteris,* and other Devonian "progymnosperms." These ancestral forms might have been heterosporous, with naked sporangia. The first seed plants had seeds that consisted of a megasporangium having one functional megaspore, with the sporangium partially enveloped by sterile appendages that did not quite cover over the sporangium. *Genomosperma* from the Lower Carboniferous is such a seedlike structure. Later specialization involved the fusing of the sterile surrounding processes to each other and, finally, to the sporangium, thus forming a more nearly typical seed.

Paleozoic pteridosperms were a diverse group, with the mono-stelic Lyginopteridaceae probably having originated from a proto-stelic ancestral type, *Microspermopteris* and *Heterangium* repre-senting primitive forms. The Medullosaceae, an unusual, polystelic group, probably had a polystelic ancestor. Primitive medullosans appear to be those with many steles and leaf traces bearing sec-ondary xylem and phloem. Permian medullosans show tangentially expanded steles; some species have a continuous outer cylinder surrounding smaller, inner steles. The Cycadales may have origi-nated from such forms.

An interesting development in the Pteridospermales was the formation of a cupulate structure surrounding one or more seeds. This cupule is also present among some of the Mesozoic pterido-sperms such as the Peltaspermaceae, Corystospermaceae, and Cay-toniaceae. In the last family mentioned the cupule closely resembles a carpel.

The Cycadeoidales and Cycadales seem to be closest to the pteridosperms, the group from which they probably arose. Mega-sporophyll evolution from pteridosperm fronds is quite obvious in the Cycadales, but the complex cones in the Cycadeoidales are much more difficult to derive from the pteridosperms.

Conifers are an ancient group that also originated early in the Paleozoic, perhaps in the Devonian. There is a remarkable simi-larity between the vegetative anatomy of an early conifer and that of one of the fernlike plants of the Devonian. *Archaeopteris-Callixylon* illustrate the difficulty in determining coniferous affinities on the basis of anatomy alone. From this plexus of fernlike plants that still retained primitive psilophytic characteristics might have originated the Cordaitales and Coniferales, two contemporary orders in the Carboniferous and Permian periods.

The ovulate cones of the Cordaitales are of interest because of their bearing on the evolution of the conifer seed cones. In *Cordai-anthus*, budlike shoots are arranged distichously in the axils of bracts on a long, slender axis. The axillary buds have spiral ap-pendages, some of which bear terminal ovules. Upper Carboniferous and Permian members of the Voltziaceae show various degrees of dorsiventral flattening, recurving of ovules, and lateral fusion, ending ultimately in a flattened, axillary, ovuliferous scale with recurving ovules borne on the upper surface. Cone scales of many modern conifers are constructed in this manner, and the seed cone may be regarded as a compound structure consisting of an axis bearing many spirally arranged axillary branches (cone scales).

Many modern conifer families were differentiated during the Mesozoic, and the group had a much wider range than at the present time.

Plants that are possibly *Ginkgo* ancestors are known from the Permian. *Trichopitys* has fertile branching axes equivalent to the ovulate stalks of the modern *Ginkgo*. Ginkgoalean leaves are common fossils of the Mesozoic, with earlier forms considerably more dissected than are the typical *Ginkgo* leaves borne on short shoots.

The origin of angiosperms, the most recent group of vascular plants to have evolved, is still uncertain. Various groups of seed plants such as conifers, Gnetales, pteridosperms, and cycadeoids, are often mentioned as possible progenitors, but no one fulfills all prerequisites of an angiosperm ancestor. Recent ideas suggest a fern ancestry for the angiosperms some time late in the Paleozoic. There appear to be more difficulties in starting with such a scheme, however, than in starting with a group of plants having seeds. Earliest angiospermlike plants occur in the Triassic, with more frequent remains in the Jurassic and Cretaceous, at the end of which period angiosperms had attained a practically world-wide distribution. Their subsequent evolution and migration patterns are quite clear but contribute little to the question of the origin of the group.

Suggestions that the angiosperms originated in uplands where chances of fossilization were poor are often presented to explain the lack of evidence of the origin of the group. While there may be some truth to this idea, it seems to be an easy way out of solving the problem. There are still many more fossils to be found and many new places to be explored, and the answer may lie hidden in the earth until a lucky find turns up a fossil or fossils that will unlock the mystery. Even though angiosperms may have originated at higher elevations, there are still good chances that fossil records of this event exist somewhere. With continued and persistent paleobotanical investigations the "abominable mystery" may yet be solved.

index

183